SUSAN LA FLESCHE PICOTTE HEALER

NANCY WALTMAN, PhD, NP

Healer: Susan La Flesche Picotte
Copyright ©2023 by Nancy Waltman, PhD, NP
Published by Four Stories Publishing.

All rights reserved. This book may not be published, broadcast, displayed or redistributed for any purpose, converted to an electronic file, e-mailed, posted on a web site, copied in any form (electronic, print, photocopy, photographed, or other means), or otherwise reproduced, licensed, transferred in any other manner without written permission from the author.

On the cover:
The bronze sculpture of Dr. Susan La Flesche Picotte is located at the Centennial Mall in Lincoln, Nebraska. The sculpture was created by Benjamin Victor and was dedicated on October 11, 2021. The sculptures and Centennial Mall are managed by the City of Lincoln Parks and Recreation Department. *Photo by Lou Waltman.*

A portion of proceeds from every sale will be given to The Walthill/Susan La Flesche Piccote Center in Walthill, Nebraska. Please consider purchasing additional copies as gifts to support this historic, Nebraska location."

Second Edition - October 2023
Printed in the United States of America.

ISBN: 979-8-9887634-0-6 (Deluxe full-color paperback edition)
979-8-9887634-2-0 (Black and white paperback edition)
979-8-9887634-1-3 (eBook edition)

Dr. Susan La Flesche Picotte Center
In Walthill, Nebraska—Formerly Walthill hospital In process of restoration. Will serve as a multipurpose facility dedicated to principals guiding the life of Susan La Flesche: "education, service, stewardship, and justice"[1] *Courtesy of Nebraska State Historical Society Photograph Collections.*

A portion of the profits from book sales will be donated to assist with restoration of the Dr. Susan La Flesche Picotte Center. The original hospital in Walthill, Nebraska that Susan had helped to build is now the Dr. Susan La Flesche Picotte Center, and the Center is in the process of restoration. While the project is well underway, much work remains to be done to restore the interior of the Center.

In the future, the Center will include a museum dedicated to the life of Dr. Susan La Flesche Picotte, a Native American Indian cultural center, a medical clinic to provide care to the

1. Benson Tong (1999). *Susan La Flesche Picotte, MD: Omaha Indian Leader and Reformer, p. 198.*

underserved, a clinic and program site for mental health and substance use disorders, a center for youth programs, and an outdoor amphitheater and community gardens. The restored Center will be a wonderful gift to the Omaha tribe of Native Americans, the citizens of Walthill, and to all Nebraskans. There is a real need for more funding to continue the restoration.

Contents

Preface

I recently retired from a 50+ year career in the medical field where I worked as a hospital nurse, educator, researcher, and nurse practitioner. I was born on a farm in Nebraska, and my great-grandparents homesteaded our family farm in Nebraska. I have always been fascinated by the state's rich history. My husband and I have resided in Lincoln, Nebraska for over forty years.

I had never heard of Dr. Susan La Flesche Picotte until 2021. In 2021, a bronze statue of Susan La Flesche Picotte was dedicated at the Centennial Mall in Lincoln, Nebraska. After doing some research, I learned that Susan La Flesche was a Native American woman who became a physician at a time before Native Americans or women had been given the right to vote. During her practice from 1890 to 1915, Susan advocated for sanitation and public health measures. She prioritized public health even before most of the public had any knowledge that germs caused diseases and before antibiotics and most vaccines were developed.

From her home in Walthill, Nebraska, Susan La Flesche fought a lifelong battle throughout Nebraska for the elimination of both tuberculosis and alcohol abuse. She fought against the injustices Native Americans were subjected to by our society. Her life was an inspiration to me, and I believed a book about her life and medical career would be inspirational to women and to all people of Nebraska. I also had some familiarity and lots of interest in the topics for this book. I had lived in Nebraska and worked in the health care field most of my life.

Beginning in 2021, I spent endless hours and several years researching the life and works of this remarkable woman. I started by visiting the many public and educational libraries in Lincoln and Omaha, Nebraska. I read the many quality books written about Susan, the Omaha tribe of Native Americans, and Nebraska history. I've listed some of the books I benefited most from reading in the Acknowledgments page.

I visited museums that featured displays about Susan La Flesche, including Durham Museum in Omaha and the Nebraska History Museum in Lincoln. I went to the Indian agency in Lincoln, Nebraska. Susan was a member of the Omaha tribe, and her medical practice was at the Macy (Omaha) reservation. My husband and I went to Walthill and spent time in both Walthill and Macy, Nebraska. We were so fortunate to be with Nancy Gillis, a Native American, who led us on a tour of the reservation. I contacted descendants of the La Flesche family, including Carolyn Johnson, the great-granddaughter of Marguerite La Flesche, and Susan Picotte, the great-granddaughter of Susan La Flesche. The people of Walthill were very gracious to us. I decided after the Walthill visit to donate a large portion of the profit from my book to restoration of the Dr. Susan La Flesche Memorial Center, located in Walthill.

Yes, writing this book has been a lengthy process. I have also learned so much. I developed a greater appreciation for the struggles of Native Americans, the courage of Susan La Flesche, and the kindness of the people of Nebraska. I want to thank you for reviewing and hopefully reading this book. Blessings to all of you.

Acknowledgments

This section was difficult for me to write because I have had the support of so many people, and I may not remember to list them all. Initially in my research, I read all the books, journal and newspaper articles, and government documents available to me. I want to especially acknowledge the following writers of the books that were critical readings for my work: Francis La Flesche & Alice Fletcher (*The Omaha Tribe*); Joe Starita (*Susan La Flesche; A Warrior of the People* and *I am a Man: Chief Standing Bear's Journey for Justice*); Benson Tong (*Susan La Flesche Picotte, MD: Omaha Indian Leader and Reformer*); Anthony Cichoke (*Secrets of Native American Herbal Remedies*); Lydia Kang & Nate Pedersen (*Patient Zero*); Michel Osterholm & Mark Olshaker (*Deadliest Enemy: Our War Against Killer Germs*);Thomas Harrison & Hillary Connery (*The Complete Family Guide to Addiction*); Judith Boughter (*Betraying the Omaha Nation 1790–1916);* Denise Lajimodiere (*Stringing Rosaries: The History, the Unforgivable, and the Healing of Northern Plains American Indian Boarding School Survivors*); and David Wishart (*Encyclopedia of the Great Plains Indians*). These books and many other readings were invaluable resources. A complete Bibliography is included at the end of this book.

Thank you to Phil Whitmarsh at *Redbrush Publishing Service*. I could not have written this book without his guidance and support. My illustrator, Erica Parker Rogers, painted wonderful and authentic pictures for use throughout the book, and I am so grateful for her help. I appreciate the support of the Indian agency in Lincoln, Nebraska. Thank you to the people I met in Walthill, Nebraska, and to descendants of the Joseph La Flesche family, especially Carolyn Johnson and Susa Picotte. Carolyn

Johnson and Susan Picotte both provided valuable information about their family. A special thank you to Nancy Gillis of Walthill, who guided my husband and me on a detailed tour of the Macy Reservation and the towns of Macy and Walthill. We also spent time at the unfinished Dr. Susan La Flesche Picotte Center. Nancy Gillis is very proud of her Native American heritage, as well she should be.

This was a family effort. I want to thank my husband Lou and my sons Luke and Clint. I wish to sincerely thank my friends, family, members of my Book Club, librarians, all the people I have consulted with, and everyone who has helped me through the process of writing this book. Truthfully, a list of the many people who helped me would be very long. So, to all of you, I truly appreciate you.

Notes

One limitation in the writing of this book is that I am not Native American. I have never lived on a reservation. To compensate, in the book, when I discussed feelings and beliefs of Native Americans, I used direct quotations from Native Americans. For example, when discussing why an understanding of the past of Native Americans is critical in understanding their present, I quoted the late renowned historian and member of the Omaha tribe, Dennis Hastings. His statement reads: "*We cannot correctly understand the present if we have a distorted interpretation of the past. Knowledge about, and correction of past injustices occurring in our nation is not simply a service to those who have been wronged, it is a service to everyone."* (A quote by Dennis Hastings in Tong, Benson (1999). *Susan La Flesche Picotte, MD: Omaha Leader and Reformer,* xii.)

The correct name for the first Native American doctor in the U.S. is Dr. Susan La Flesche Picotte. In 1894, Susan La Flesche married Henry Picotte, a member of the Yankton Sioux tribe. However, throughout this book, Susan will be referred to as Susan La Flesche. Her last name, Picotte, will be omitted for the purposes of brevity.

Also, in the book, the term "White Americans" is synonymous with the terms "European Americans" and "Anglo Americans." Most of the original Nebraska settlers were from Europe.

In various writings, Susan's sister's name is spelled either as "Susette" or "Suzette." Of course, both spellings refer to the same person.

I do not recommend that readers use the herbal treatments described in the book without further consultation. Just as prescribed medications often have adverse side effects, herbal treatments can also have adverse effects.

Finally, in researching this book, I've reviewed hundreds of books, journal and newspaper articles, government documents, and letters, and I've discussed my book with multiple Native Americans. Recalls and interpretations of history that were included in readings were sometimes inconsistent. Primary sources describing American history prior to the 1900s were not always available. I omitted content from the book when research was contradictory or not well-supported. For example, in my readings, numerous incidents were described when Europeans and Anglo Americans provided to Native Americans blankets contaminated with smallpox. Most of these incidents could not be confirmed. I included only one incident in my book, and this was at Fort Pitt. The British General Amherst had approved giving blankets and a handkerchief contaminated with smallpox to the Ottawa tribe to "*rid the nation of all Indians*." A letter written to Amherst and other evidence confirmed to my satisfaction that this incident had occurred. To the best of my ability, all the content I have included in this book is accurate.

Introduction

This book describes Dr. Susan La Flesche Picotte as a physician for her "Umaha" (Omaha) people, and as a leader and advocate for her people, fighting for their survival. She fought for their causes, and many times the fight was against her own U.S. government.

The book tells four stories.

The first story is about the Omaha people, their history as a noble tribe, and their challenges in interacting with a white culture that invaded their territory. When the white traders and settlers came to Nebraska, the Native Americans had to learn a new language, a new culture, and most importantly, new ways to protect their families and provide food for them.

The Omaha tribe were peaceful and had never taken up arms against the U.S. government. Too often, however, our U.S. leaders treated all American Indians the same way—as hostiles. U.S leaders spoke of "Manifest Destiny," the belief that the expansion of the U.S. throughout the American continent was both justified and inevitable. Native Americans were believed to be impeding this "Destiny" by objecting to white settlers on their land.

The second story describes deadly infectious diseases that were brought to the continent by Europeans, and that have greatly impacted Omaha people as well as all Native Americans. The Omaha people had no "host immunity" against infectious diseases such as smallpox. Prior to the discovery that germs caused diseases and the development of vaccines and antibiotics, infectious diseases were the greatest killers of indigenous people throughout history. One of Susan's greatest contributions as a provider of medical care was to teach sanitation measures to her tribe to prevent the spread of germs. Susan's emphasis on sanitary procedures such as hand washing, isolation of the sick, and use of clean water most certainly saved thousands of lives.

The third story is about Dr. Susan La Flesche Picotte and her family. In 1889, at the age of twenty-four, Susan graduated from the Women's Medical College in Philadelphia, Pennsylvania, and became the first Native American doctor in U.S. history. Susan's family, her early years, and her medical education are described. There are anecdotes of Susan's work as a medical provider. She was also a leader of her Omaha people and an advocate for their welfare. She helped her people to understand land deeds, to read English, and to communicate their needs to the Indian agents. She met with legislators, and even travelled to Washington, D.C. (District of Columbia) to champion the cause of the Omaha people.

The fourth story examines "historical or intergenerational trauma" as one cause of mental health and societal problems that continue to be experienced by Omaha people today. The U.S. is a great nation, with a strong military and economy. Our forefathers provided a sound foundation for growth and progression. However, because of the white "invasion" as well as actions of our forefathers, Native Americans have lost a large percentage of both their land and their population. Many of them still retain the scars of their tragic experiences at Federal Boarding Schools. The first settlers of our land, the indigenous people, the Native Americans, have suffered great losses since the 1700s. Americans today can help them to heal from this "trauma of the soul." The Omaha people are surviving. With our help, and the help of their leaders, they can continue to progress.

The following paragraphs are short summaries of the ten chapters in the book. Chapter one examines the Omaha people, their history, their traditions, and their challenges. The chapter describes their migration from the east coast, their life on the upper Missouri River, their philosophy of health, and their use of herbal therapies and sweat lodges. One spiritual object that the people believed unified them as a tribe was the Sacred Pole. The Omaha people were a noble tribe who worked together for the common good. They planted and harvested crops and gathered wild plants to use both for food and for herbal treatments. They depended heavily on the buffalo for their food, clothing, and shelter. They shared their bounties with all members of the tribe.

Chapter two describes the challenges faced by the Omaha people resulting from the demise of the buffalo, the invasion of the white settlers, and the tribe's confinement to the reservation. The Treaty of 1854, signed by both the U.S. government and the Omaha tribe, required the Omaha people to move to the Macy reservation. The Homestead Act of 1862 and the beginning of the Intercontinental Railroad in 1869 hastened the movement of white settlers west.

It can be argued that whites settling on the western frontier were a necessary progression in the development of our nation. Development of the frontier helped make the U.S. a great and wealthy country. Unfortunately, in their interaction with the Plains tribes, government leaders too often treated the Native Americans unfairly and as second-class citizens.

During the post-Civil War period, there were numerous battles between the more warlike tribes on the Plains and the U.S. Cavalry. Examples were the "Battle at Little Bighorn" and the "Wagon Train Raid." Hostilities resulted in the U.S. government and Cavalry becoming even more punitive toward all Native Americans. All tribes were treated the same way, even though the Omaha tribe had always been peaceful.

U.S. leaders wanted to "rid the tribes of their Indian ways. "The Dawes Act in 1877 was passed with the goal of weakening tribal unity and ridding the Omaha people of their culture and traditions. With reservation life, the once physically strong Omaha people encountered malnutrition and illness. Prior to Susan La Flesche, the medical care the people received from the white agency doctors was less than adequate.

Chapter three describes the early life of Susan La Flesche and her preparation as a physician. Susan La Flesche's family, her heritage as a member of the Omaha tribe, and her medical education was examined to help understand why she was so suited for providing medical care to this population.

Susan's sister "Susette" took part in two of the most significant incidents in the 1800s that involved the U.S. government and Native Americans. The first was the "Trial of Standing Bear." Standing Bear was imprisoned because he and thirty of his followers left the reservation in Oklahoma to return to their home in Nebraska. Susette's husband, Thomas Tibbles, was instrumental in initiating a trial arguing "the right of a citizen to obtain a writ of *habeas corpus* as a protection against illegal imprisonment." In other words, Standing Bear should not have been imprisoned by the government and should have been allowed the choice to leave the reservation. Susette served as interpreter of Standing Bear during the trial. The judge ruled in favor of Standing Bear, that Native Americans should have the same rights as all people in the U.S. Standing Bear was allowed to return to his home in Nebraska. During the trial, he spoke the infamous words "*My blood is the same color as your blood. I am a man.*"[1] Susette was also at the Lakota Sioux camp during the tragic "Massacre at Wounded Knee" when hundreds of Sioux women and children were chased and gunned down by out-of-control Cavalry men. For her many contributions to Native Americans, she obtained national prominence as their advocate.

Chapter three also describes Susan's provision of medical care for her tribal patients. There were many limitations to medical care in the 1890s. Susan used both modern or prescription medicines and the herbal therapies she had learned from the traditional healers from the tribe. She also believed in the Native American philosophy of health, "*Healing the body must first begin with healing the spirit. True healing can only occur when the body and spirit are in balance.*"[2]

During her time providing medical care for her tribal patients, Susan sutured cuts, straightened broken bones, and cared for patients with common colds as well as patients with life-threatening infectious diseases. She assisted women and their babies during childbirth. She was concerned about her patients' mental health needs and their problems with aging. Susan fought for a hospital on the reservation. The opening of the Walthill hospital in 1913 was considered one of Susan's greatest accomplishments.

By today's standards, diagnostic tools and medical therapies in the 1800s were primitive. When Susan practiced as a physician, over 95 percent of the medications used today were not available. She used all the modern medicines and herbal therapies available to her to relieve symptoms of disease such as fever, cough, pain, and stomach disorders.

Chapter four describes medications available in the 1890s, as well as describing growing concerns about opiate addictions. No antibiotics were available for treating infectious diseases, and the only vaccine available was for smallpox.

The importance of developing antibiotics and vaccines became apparent when "germs" were discovered as the cause of infections. With discovery of the "germ theory," there was also a greater awareness of the importance of sanitation. Chapter five describes how newly acquired knowledge of the "germ theory" during the 1890s influenced Susan's decision to promote public health and sanitation. Compared to Anglo Americans, Native Americans had little awareness of the importance of sanitation in preventing disease. Once sanitation procedures were implemented on the reservation, thousands of lives were saved.

Chapters, six, seven, and eight describe Susan La Flesche's care of her patients with life-threatening infectious diseases that have caused the death of so many Native Americans. These diseases included tuberculosis, influenza, smallpox, measles, typhoid fever, cholera, and dysentery. The symptoms and cause of these diseases are examined as well as their management in the 1890s and their current incidence and management. Anecdotes will be shared describing Susan's approach to caring for patients with these diseases.

During her time as medical provider, Susan observed the depression and sense of loss in members of her tribe. She was especially concerned about the emerging problem of alcohol abuse in tribal members and the damage this problem was causing on the reservation. Chapter nine describes cultural and economic *"dispossession"*[3] and "historical trauma" as compelling causes for depression and alcohol addiction in Native Americans. Strategies for prevention and management of historical trauma are also examined.

Chapter ten is a summary of life on the Macy reservation today. The towns of Macy and Walthill are the centers of reservation life. Compared to Nebraskans who are not Native American, Omaha people continue to have more physical and mental health problems, more problems with alcohol and substance abuse, and higher poverty levels. However, attitudes of Americans and the policies of the U.S. government are changing. In recent times, the U.S. government, as well as Non-Native Americans, have recognized that they have been a part of the abuse of the indigenous people and have tried to make amends. Today, U.S. leaders are striving to incorporate Native Americans into our society as knowledgeable, empowered, and belonging equals. In addition, the Omaha people are blessed with good leaders who are helping the tribe to grow and progress. The Omaha people are surviving. They are here to stay.

The following is a quote from the works of David Wishart (2007).[4]

> *Omaha Indians continue to negotiate their lives between the pressures of life in mainstream Western society and the traditional values of the Omaha Indian culture. Leaders of the tribe continue to emerge out of this struggle to help their people as they navigate the challenges ahead. "Umaha" people were named for their ability to travel the waters "upstream," or against the current. Because of the strength and dignity of the people and their leaders, the Omaha Indians will continue to travel upstream as a proud nation.*

ONE

The History and Culture of the Omaha People

This story will begin with the Umaha (Omaha) tribe migrating west to the Nebraska Territory.

The Omaha tribe originally resided in the Ohio River Valley, near the present-day city of Cincinnati, Ohio.[1] In the late 1600s and early 1700s, the tribe migrated to the upper Missouri River area as well as the grass covered prairies of northeast Nebraska. This area is now the location of the Macy Reservation.

Because the soil was fertile and the rainfall was adequate, this area was well-suited for growing crops. Occasionally droughts did occur, however, and throughout history there have been stories of swarms of grasshoppers who destroyed the planted crops. The summers were hot and the winters cold. In January, the temperature could reach lows of -20°F. There could be snow, blizzards, sleet, and ice. The Omaha people called January the month "*when the snow drifts into the tents.*"[2] There are anecdotes of Susan La Flesche riding on horseback or in her buggy visiting patients on the reservation when the temperature was below freezing, with two to four feet of snow on the ground. Even though she wore heavy shawls, mufflers, and covered herself with buffalo robes during the visits, her ears and face still felt the cold.

The Omaha tribe called themselves "U-Mo'n-Ho'n" —meaning "people who travel upstream" or against the current.[3] In 1718, French cartographer Guillaume Delisle named the tribe "the Maha," meaning "a wandering nation." Later the French name "Maha" evolved to Umaha and Omaha.

In the 1700s, the Omaha tribe was considered among the most powerful of the tribes in Nebraska.[4] One reason for this is that they were effectively using horses in both hunting and warfare. Horses were introduced to America by the Spanish, and they began to be used by the Plains tribes in the 1600's. The introduction of horses had far-reaching cultural, economic, and political effects for the Omaha people.[5] Members of the Omaha tribe who owned the most horses were considered to have wealth and a position of power. Horses were extremely useful on buffalo hunts, and they allowed the Omaha people to interact more with other tribes as well as with the European and French-Canadian fur traders.

In the 1700s, the Omaha tribe had developed a fur trading network along the Missouri River with European and French-Canadian explorers. They first developed friendly relations with the French in the mid seventeenth century, followed by the British, and the Americans.[6] The Spanish had also built a fort near the Omaha villages and had traded regularly with the Omaha during this period.[7]

The permanent homes for the Omaha tribal families were earth lodges.[8] These were semi-subterranean buildings covered partially or totally by earth. Their dome shaped structure was obtained using angled or carefully bent tree limbs, generally from cottonwood trees. The inner shell of the dome could be made up of long grasses and willow. The outer shell often consisted of clay. The earth lodge had a firepit in the middle of the shell with a smoke hole on top of it. Earth lodges could be made in various sizes to accommodate the size of the family, and the diameter of the lodge could vary anywhere from forty to ninety feet.

Every spring, after crops were planted, the Omaha people went on buffalo hunts. On the hunts, loads of food and supplies and portable tents or tipis were carried by horses. Before horses were used, the Indians had dogs for hauling their loads. Compared to dogs, horses could haul loads that were four times heavier, and horses could travel twice as far in a day.

Plains Tribe Earth Home. Shuttlestock.

Dogs continued to be used to carry small items on travels.

Tipis were conical tents made of animal hides or pelts stretched on a framework of wooden poles. They were durable, warm in the winter, cool in the summer, and they kept the Indians dry during heavy rainfalls. Most importantly, they were easy to mantle and dismantle, fitting the nomadic lifestyle of the Omaha people.[9]

Life was not easy for the people, but they survived.[10] The weather was unpredictable and could be deadly, food could be hard to find, and conflict with other tribes was always a danger. The men provided for and protected their families.[11] They hunted for food, protected the tribe from the Sioux and Anglo American intruders, and helped with planting and harvesting the crops. Women did most of the work in planting and harvesting as well as gathering wild fruits and vegetables. They cared for the children, prepared the buffalo hides, sewed the family's clothing, carried wood for the fire and water for drinking and washing, and cooked the food.[12] Historically, the Omaha people considered all members of the tribe as their family. The good of the tribe always prevailed over the desires of the individual. Despite their many challenges, the people shared their meat and vegetable bounties with others in the tribe, and all tribal members helped the elderly, the vulnerable, and the children.

Women had no voice on the Tribal Council. Unlike Anglo American women in the Victorian Era, however, Omaha women were well respected by the tribe.[13] Women managed all household affairs and owned the earth lodge and all its contents. They were free to marry who they wished and had the power to divorce. Women who wanted to end a marriage often just placed their husband's belongings outside the lodge and the marriage was over. Before they were married, young girls in the village were never left unprotected.[14]

The Omaha families loved their children.[15] *"Children were considered the most precious possessions of the Omaha tribal family."*[16] When signing treaties or making decisions about their tribes, tribal leaders would always express concerns about the future of their children. Omaha children knew both love and discipline. Each child was disciplined and trained to take their place in the family and the tribe. Children were told stories to emphasize the important qualities of truth and dependability. They were taught to respect their elders and to address them courteously. When in the presence of adults, they were to play quietly and speak in low tones. They were taught to say thank you when a gift was given to them. Girls were trained by their mothers and grandmothers while boys were trained by their fathers, uncles, and grandfathers. In the spring, women and children sowed corn, hoed potatoes, and weeded. In the fall, they helped with the harvest. Girls also swept the floor, foraged for wood, dressed animal skins, dried bison meat, and carried water to the camp from a nearby stream.[17] Boys were also taught how to make tools and to help defend their tribe. Many boys were provided their own bow and arrow at the age of four.

Members of the Omaha tribe have traditionally showed respect and reverence for older tribal members. The elderly were honored for their knowledge and wisdom, and they often served as teachers for the young

The livelihood of Omaha people depended on the buffalo.

During the 1700s and most of the 1800s, buffaloes provided the Omaha people with food, clothing, blankets, rope, moccasins, fuel, shelter, and utensils. In addition to hunting buffalo, however, Omaha's also fished and hunted for beaver, rabbits, deer, elk, and turkey. Food staples planted

Buffalo. Shuttlestock.

included corn, squash, beans, potatoes, pumpkins, and watermelon. The food staples most often used were maize (corn), squash, and beans. Women used the squash to make sweet golden pies.[18]

For meals, Omaha people used foods in the wild as well as foods they had harvested. Foods that grew "wild" in the area included onions, Indian rice, mushrooms, wild turnips, artichokes, strawberries, mulberries, raspberries, and plums. The Omaha people generally only had two meals a day.[19]A typical meal included meat stew (buffalo, rabbit, or deer meat),[20] fry bread,[21] and foods made with corn (maize). A common meat product was "pemmican," which consisted of finely ground buffalo meat, melted fat, and fruit, nuts, or honey. Omaha Indians believed that no plants, animals, or land should be wasted. Even the roots of plants were ground into powders for use in breads and other foods.

George Catlin—An artist who painted the Nebraska scenery and portraits of Omaha tribal people.[22.]

Images of the inhabitants and landscape of Nebraska in the 1800s were best preserved by painters and illustrators (artists) of the time. One such famous artist was George Catlin.

Catlin was born in Philadelphia in 1796 and was originally educated to become a lawyer. He became a painter instead and made the decision to focus his oil paintings on portraits of Native Americans and their lifestyle. In the years 1832 and 1833, he travelled down the Missouri River and painted pictures of Indian tribes as well as the river, the trees, and the prairies.

Along with his paintings, Catlin wrote about what he perceived as the beauty of the Nebraska prairie country. In his writings, he described the green grass, sloping hills, and clusters of trees along the upper Missouri, and the richness of the soil. Before he died in 1872, Catlin had visited forty-eight Native American tribes and painted over five hundred pictures. He is famous for his portraits, and he painted Native Americans as strong and noble human beings. He was a romantic who painted the Omaha people when they looked their best and in their finest costumes. The largest collection of Catlin's paintings is at the Smithsonian Institution in Washington, D.C.

Paintings by George Catlin
Courtesy of Smithsonian Art Gallery, Washington, D.C., —Open Access.

Big Elk—Ongpatonga
Principal Chief of Omaha tribe of Native Americans in Nebraska (1770–1846). Struggled to protect his people from encroachment by white settlers and from warfare with the Sioux. Courtesy of Smithsonian.

(Left)
Double Walker—Nobamonnee
Omaha brave Double Walker wears a buffalo robe and leggings fringed with scalp locks. His hair is dressed in a single feather that may indicate he was a warrior. George Catlin painted this portrait at Fort Leavenworth, Kansas, in 1832. (Gurney and Heyman, eds., George Catlin, and His Indian Gallery, 2002) Courtesy of Smithsonian

(Below)
Buffalo Chase with Bows and Arrows
George Catlin sketched this scene on the Upper Missouri in 1832. (Catlin, Letters and Notes, vol. 1, no. 31, 1841; reprint 1973). Courtesy of Smithsonian.

Batiste, Bogard, and I approaching Buffalo on the Missouri
"Batiste, Bogard, and Catlin went ashore at the Upper Missouri with rifles and shot a buffalo for food" Sketched in 1932. (Catlin, Letters and Notes, vol. 2, no. 32, 1841; reprint 1973) Courtesy of Smithsonian.

Blackbird's Grave, a Back View, Prairies Enameled with flowers
Blackbird's grave, a site visited by Lewis and Clark in 1804, was the final resting-place for Omaha chief Blackbird, who had been buried astride his favorite horse. The artist painted this work in 1832 on his first extended voyage up the Missouri River. Courtesy of Smithsonian.

Belle Vue, Indian agency of Major Dougherty, 870 Miles above St. Louis.
In the 1830s, The Bellevue Indian agency, located on the western shore of the Missouri River, served Native Americans from the Omaha, Oto, Pawnee, and Missouri tribes. According to Catlin, this 1832 painting depicts a beautiful land surrounded with cornfields, potatoes, and numerous fruit trees. (Catlin, Letters and Notes, vol. 2, no. 32, 1841). Courtesy of Smithsonian.

The Native American Philosophy of Health[23]

Native Americans were and are a spiritual people. Their lives and beliefs were guided by their spirituality. They believed that all things in nature, including humans, animals, plants, land, and water, were gifts entrusted to them by their Creator—the Great Spirit or "Wakonda." Humans were not at the center of nature. They were only a part of the whole. All things in nature were related to the land, and land was the "breath of life." Without land, there was no spiritual energy. Physical and spiritual healing was only possible through the Great Spirit. In addition to humans, healing was also needed for the land, air, water, plants, and other animals. Historically, illnesses in Native Americans were treated by traditional healers (medicine men and women), and herbal therapies were frequently used to promote healing.

Healers were often very secretive about the herbal therapies they used. Recipes have not been well documented, and many of them have been lost over the years. The following paragraphs describe herbs grown in northeast Nebraska that could have been used by the Omaha people and by Susan La Flesche for healing.

Use of Herbal Therapies

Herbs are defined as any plants that were used by the Indians as medical therapy.[24] Herbal treatments were administered by medicine men or women as teas, powders, poultices, compresses, ointments, or washes. Teas were generally made by combining all the healing herbs in a glass container and covering with water. The liquid was steeped for about thirty minutes and the herbs were strained from the liquid. Sometimes honey was added to the liquid to improve the taste of the tea. The water was warmed for drinking, and patients were told to drink one-half to one cup of tea every six hours. Powdered herbs were made by drying the herbs and grinding or crushing them. The resultant powder could be formed into tablets. This powder could also be added to teas. Ointments were made by placing about three ounces of dried herbs in a pot and simmering in buffalo fat. The mixture was heated for at least two hours, and the dried herbs were then strained from the mixture. If the consistency still didn't have the solidity of an ointment, beeswax was added.

Poultices were hot, moist herbal concentrations made by applying a semi-liquid mass of herbs and buffalo fat directly on the skin for moisture, heat, and healing. Compresses were made by mixing ground herbs with water, pouring the mixture over a loose cloth, and then pressing the cloth directly on the skin. Eye washes, commonly used to decrease pain from inflamed eyes, were made by combining boiling water with herbs and steeping for ten to fifteen minutes. Herbs were strained from the liquid, the liquid was cooled, and the resulting eyewash was used to flush out the eyes.

Herbal Plants in Nebraska

The following are descriptions of selected herbs in the Missouri River region that were used in herbal therapies. Illustrations by Erica Parker Rogers.

Corn Silk. *(Stigma maydis)*. The fine yellow threads found at the tip of an ear of corn were ground and added to a tea or poultice that was used to treat bladder problems and premenstrual symptoms and could also be used to soothe irritated tissues.[25]

Dandelions *(Taraxacum officinal)* are perennial, small, yellow flowering plants that are found everywhere. Today, they are widely considered weeds to be eliminated. Indians ingested ground dandelions to treat water retention (as a diuretic) and to treat constipation (as a laxative). Dandelions were also applied to the skin to treat problems such as rashes and irritation.[26]

The **Goldenrod** *(Solidago virgaurea)* is a yellow flowering perennial plant four feet in height. This plant has been designated as the "Nebraska state flower" and has been used for herbal therapy for hundreds of years. Even today, goldenrod products are commonly sold as herbal supplements in health food stores. Goldenrod products were ingested by Native Americans for prevention and treatments of coughs, colds, and sore throats; for prevention and treatment of diarrhea; and were used in warm compresses to treat burns, skin ulcers, strained muscles, and to stop bleeding wounds.[27]

Pleurisy roots *(Asclepias tuberosa)* are orange flowering weeds and members of the milkweed family. They were eaten raw and used to treat lung problems. They have also been named "butterfly weeds" because their nectar and orange color attract butterflies. [28]

The **Raspberry** *(Rubus idaeus)* plant is perennial, grows one foot in height, and can become quite invasive. While

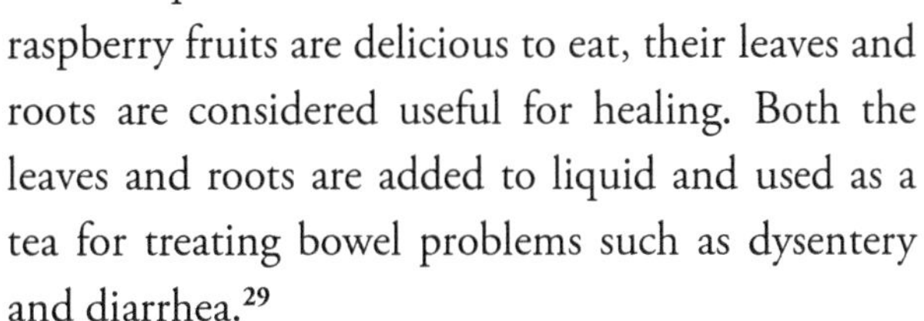

raspberry fruits are delicious to eat, their leaves and roots are considered useful for healing. Both the leaves and roots are added to liquid and used as a tea for treating bowel problems such as dysentery and diarrhea.[29]

The **Strawberry** *(Fragaria vesca)* plant is perennial and found in grasslands. Traditionally, strawberries were used as a laxative (to promote bowel movements) and as a diuretic (to promote voiding or urination). The fruit has antioxidant properties which means they may be effective in preventing cancer and blood clotting.[30]

The **Sunflower** *(Helianthus annuus)* is a flowering plant that adds to the beauty of Nebraska fields every fall and

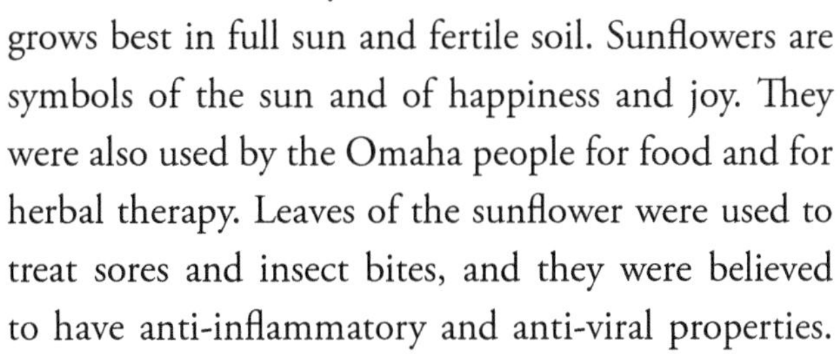

grows best in full sun and fertile soil. Sunflowers are symbols of the sun and of happiness and joy. They were also used by the Omaha people for food and for herbal therapy. Leaves of the sunflower were used to treat sores and insect bites, and they were believed to have anti-inflammatory and anti-viral properties.

Flower heads with seeds were used to treat malaria, stomach, and lung problems, coughs, colds, and rheumatism.[31]

The **Sweet Flag** *(Acorus calamus)* is a sweet-smelling perennial plant that has thin, grass-like green leaves with yellow variegation. It grows best in shady, moist soil, and can be found around ponds, streams, and woodlands. The Omaha people held this plant in very high esteem. It was used for coughs, fever, colds, toothaches, and colic. The plant has been ascribed with mystic powers and is used as a garland around the neck.[32]

Sweet grass *(Hierochloe odorata)* is an aromatic herb found commonly in northeastern Nebraska. It grows best in shady, moist soil, and can be found around ponds, streams, and woodlands. True to its name, the crushed foliage of sweet grass is sweet smelling. This herb was used to treat asthma.[33]

Wild plum. *(Prunus americana).* Every year, the Omaha people planted their corn, beans, and squash when the wild plums came into bloom. Omaha people ate this delicious purple fruit raw or cooked in a sauce. The plums were also dried for winter use. The barks of the wild plum roots were boiled, and compresses were applied as a remedy for abrasions of the skin.[34]

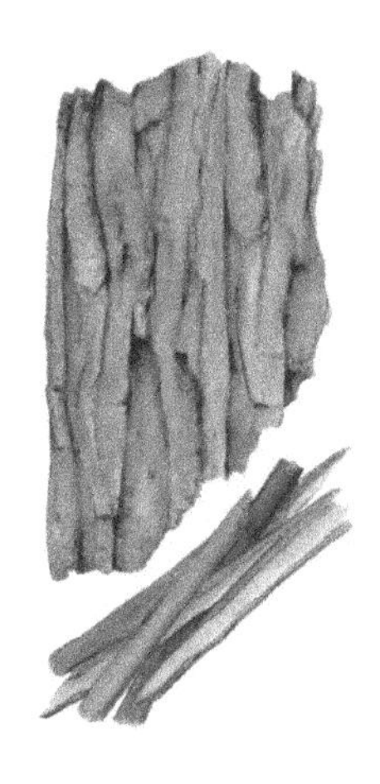

Willow bark. *(Salicis)*. The leaf and bark of the willow tree were used to treat pain and fever. Willow trees require sun and plenty of moisture and are known to be present in Nebraska—especially the Black Willow tree. Aspirin contains salicin, and salicin is obtained from the willow bark.[35]

Yarrow. *(Achillea millefolium)***.** The leaf of the Yarrow plant was made into a wash and used by the Winnebago people to bathe swellings. The leaves were believed to relieve earaches when a wad of the leaves was put into the ear.[36]

History of Herbal Therapies

There has been written evidence of the use of plants for healing as early as 3,000 BC. In early times, the Chinese wrote about illness as an imbalance between yin and yang. Herbs were used to restore balance in the body and to adjust the body's energy flow.

Many of the prescribed drugs derived from plants that were used by Susan La Flesche in the 1880s are still used today. These include opium and morphine (from poppy or *Papaver somniferous*); cocaine (*Erythroxylum coca*); quinine (*Cinchona bark);* and digitalis (*Digitalis purpurea*, a species of foxglove). Some of the key anti-cancer drugs used today are derived from plants. These include vincristine and vinblastine (from periwinkle or *Catharanthus roseus*); and paclitaxel (Pacific yew or *Taxus brevifolia*). Currently, daffodil bulbs (*Narcissus* species) are studied for their usefulness in treating Alzheimer's disease symptoms.[37]

There are an estimated 300,000 to 400,000 species of terrestrial plants worldwide, and 35,500 have been used for medicinal use. [38] Forty percent of the prescribed medicines today come from plants. In addition, many herbal supplements are available without prescriptions and are sold as alternative therapies.

Native Americans believed that healing could only occur when the patient's mind and spirit were in balance.[39] Herbs could be used to return balance. However, herbal treatments were only one of the many ways to return balance and to heal the sick and injured. Native Americans were strong believers in spiritual powers that were not well understood, and these spiritual powers could aide them or cause them great harm. They used prayers, chants, and rituals to drive away harmful spirits any time there was a need to protect their people from these spirits. Thus, prayer and chants were used to prevent and treat illness, to increase the chance of success during warfare, when women were birthing children, and when Native Americans entered the sweat lodges for healing.

Sweat Lodges[40]

Sweat lodges were low-profile huts and often were dome-shaped or oblong. Much like a sauna, the sweat lodge's heat and moisture were used to heal the body—mentally, physically, and spiritually. When Native Americans were in the lodge, a ceremony was conducted that included prayers and songs. Spirits in the lodge were believed to cleanse and purify the participants. They assisted in the search for solutions to mental, physical, and spiritual needs. The lodge provided the opportunity to pray, speak, and ask for forgiveness, both from the Creator and from people they may have physically hurt. The frames of sweat lodges consisted of willow or sapling poles covered by buffalo or other animal skins. The lodge was frequently four feet high in the center, and a pit was built in the center for sacred fires. Rocks were added to the burning fire, and water was poured over the rocks to create steam. Sweat lodges continue to be used by Omaha people today.

The Sacred Pole[41]

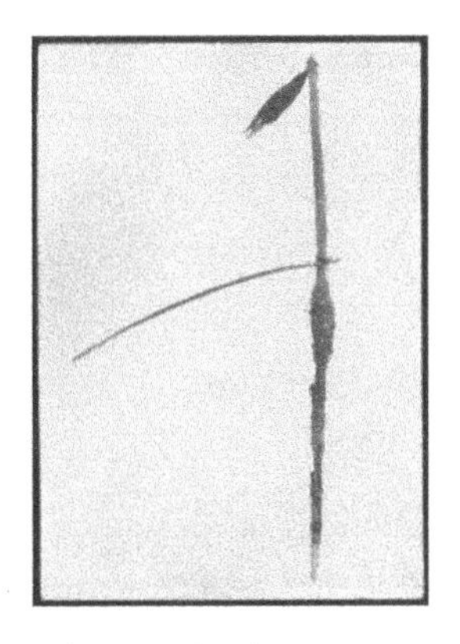

The Sacred Pole (Umon'hon'ti or "Venerable Man")
Nebraska State Historical Society Photograph Collections.

Along with rituals, prayers, and chants, and as part of their spiritual beliefs, the Omaha people revered spiritual items which they believed protected their tribal unity. One such item was an ancient Sacred Pole (Umon'hon'ti or "Venerable Man"). This Sacred Pole was cut from a cotton wood tree. Later it was trimmed, painted, and hair was attached to the top of the tree; the pole was said to represent the body of a man.

The Omaha people saw the pole as a person—a man who would provide for and protect their people throughout their travels. He (the pole) migrated with them to their home on the Missouri River. The tribe carried the pole with them when they went on buffalo hunts. He was with the Omaha tribe when they traded their furs along the Missouri. He accompanied the tribe during the years of war and diseases. Through conflict and sickness, he never deserted them. The pole was kept in a Sacred Tent in the center of the village, and only men who were members of the Holy Society could enter the Sacred Tent.

In 1888, the tribe sent the Sacred Pole to the Peabody Museum at Harvard University for protection. About a hundred years later, in July 1989, the pole was again returned to the Omaha tribe, and a powwow was held to celebrate its return. The Omaha people believe that the Sacred Pole ensures their continued survival. They also believe they can only survive by continuing their traditions and by honoring their heritage. The following is a quotation from the book "*Blessing for a Long Time: The Sacred Pole of the Omaha Tribe,*"[42]

> *Generations of white colonizers and their descendants have predicted that Native Americans were a "vanishing race." But as the five hundredth anniversary of the Columbus voyage recedes into history,*

indigenous people are still a vital presence in the land. . . . They survive in ceremonies and prayers. They survive with the Sacred Pole. They survive when they conclude a sweat or ceremony by saying "All my relations." They survive in cities and on reservations. They survive as nations. They survive.

Quackery and Drug Addiction among Native Americans / Omaha People

Some of the herbal therapies used by the Omaha people were not effective or useful and may have been dangerous. Precautions were always needed when therapies were administered to pregnant women or children. In her clinical practice, Susan La Flesche only used herbal medicines that she was familiar with, and only when she had observed these therapies to be effective. Susan was most likely to use herbal therapies when prescription or modern medicines were not effective or available.

Except for alcohol, legal and illegal drug abuses were relatively rare on the reservation. While whiskey peddlers were continually selling their wares on the reservation, most Omaha people had not been introduced to many of the other addictive drugs such as morphine or the opiate derivate "Laudanum." Unfortunately, the Omaha people today are still plagued with an alcohol and drug abuse problems—especially with use of the drugs marijuana, cocaine, and methamphetamines. "Historical Trauma" as one probable cause of these abuses will be discussed in chapter nine.

Peyote—A Hallucinogenic Drug

One drug used by the Omaha people as early as the 1900s and of special concern to Susan La Flesche was "peyote" a small, spineless cactus that has blue-green buttons and sporadically produces pink or white flowers.[43] The plant originated in Mexico and the southwest U.S. and contains mescaline, which has hallucinogenic properties. Peyote can be prepared as a tea by using the leaves and roots of the plant. Native Americans can also ingest dried, brown peyote or mescaline (mescal) buttons, about the size of a quarter. Sometimes peyote can cause nausea and stomach upset when taken by mouth. When this occurs, peyote can also be administered as an enema.

Peyote is believed to have been used by the indigenous populations since the 1500s. Most likely, peyote was so popular because it appeals to the Native American's sense of the mysterious and the supernatural. Peyote triggers rich, brilliantly colored visual and auditory effects and spiritual insights, and effects from ingestion of the peyote buttons can last 12 hours. When people take peyote, they enter a "trance-like" state. The effects of peyote are like the effects observed today with use of the hallucinogenic drug LSD (*Lysergic acid diethylamide*).

Peyote was used in religious rituals by the Native American Church. Leaders of the church included many of the historic Christian beliefs in their teachings. In addition to the teachings, however, the church included rituals using peyote. Peyote was ingested during a formal, all-night prayer meeting typically held in a tipi or special house. There was singing, drumming, and praying while the peyote was ingested. Church members referred to peyote as "sacred medicine" and used it to combat spiritual, physical, and social ills.

The Omaha people were introduced to peyote by the Otoe tribe of Native Americans in 1906. They were told that use of peyote could cure "alcohol addiction." The religion soon became quite popular on the reservation. By 1911, it was reported that at least half the Omaha tribe followed the "peyote" religion. Indians believed that besides its use in curing addiction, peyote was a way to salvage and retain their traditions and culture. They also believed that the spiritual power peyote offered was only attainable using the Native American Church protocol. Thus, peyote was advocated only for religious purposes and not for recreational use.

From the beginning, in 1906, Susan was opposed to the use of peyote and the Native American Church. She told her people that ingestion of peyote and mescaline were dangerous, addictive, and as culturally destructive as alcohol. She publicly fought against the drug and induced the U.S. government to stop importing peyote from Mexico. Susan was reported to say to her people that "*the mescal bean is a great evil.*"[44]

The Omaha people believed that peyote was the very thing that could save the tribe, and they could not understand why Susan and the U.S. government wanted to keep peyote from them. This incident was one time when the Omaha people viewed Susan La Flesche as a "sellout." It appeared she had become "too white" and to no longer value the Native American culture. This was disappointing to Susan because she had fought so hard to help her people to maintain their heritage while interacting with the white culture.

Susan's belief about the dangers of peyote changed over the years. In the diary Susan kept in 1910 and 1911, Susan recorded that some Omaha people had been sharing with her the positive impact of peyotism in their lives. She observed that these people had given up drinking, were building new homes, and were beginning to save their money. She believed in her Presbyterian Christianity, but she was no longer opposed to the Native American Church. By 1914, Susan was no longer fighting the battle against peyote. She continued to battle against alcoholism throughout her lifetime, however.

Studies have been conducted examining the damaging effects of peyote. In 2007, a study of Native Americans found that peyote use was not related to long-term learning problems. Although rare, a few episodes of psychotic breaks with peyote use have occurred in Indians who already had mental health problems. Peyote can cause potentially serious variations in heart rate, blood pressure, and breathing. Also, peyote should not be used by pregnant women because there may be harm to unborn babies. It is still not known whether peyote is useful to prevent or treat alcohol abuse.

Ever since its introduction in the Native American Church in the mid-1800s, the use of peyote has been controversial. Some Americans (both Native Americans and whites) believe that peyote use should be banned completely. Others believe the opposite—that peyote should be legal and that the drug could be effective in fighting depression, mental illnesses, and addictions. The US government agrees that, for the members of the Native American Church, peyote is not seen as a mind-altering hallucinogenic drug, but rather as a medicine of healing. The 1994 amendment to the American Indian Religious Freedom Act legalized the use of peyote for that purpose—to be used as part of the church service only, and not as a recreational drug.[45]

Currently, the Native American Church remains active on the Macy Reservation, and peyote is used in services. In the U.S., peyote is a controlled drug. The importation, possession, and use of peyote for "bona fide religious ceremonies" is allowed for members of the Native American Church only. Any person who manufactures peyote for or distributes peyote to the Native American Church is required to obtain registration annually and to comply with all other requirements of the law.

During the 1800s, the Omaha people faced numerous challenges.

In 1758, there were 3,200 Omaha Native American people living in forty villages. The Omaha tribe was most powerful between 1775 and 1800, largely because of their leader, Chief Blackbird. Blackbird was an autocratic leader and reported to be ruthless to tribal members who opposed him. He also believed that fostering good relations with European explorers and traders was the key to survival for the Omaha tribe. He knew that the Omaha people lacked a large population as defense from neighboring tribes, and he used trade with the Spanish and French as a security measure to protect his people. Under his leadership, the Omaha tribe was powerful and feared by other tribes. This changed when the tribe suffered a smallpox epidemic in 1800. One-third of the tribal members died from smallpox, including Blackbird.

After the smallpox epidemic and Blackbird's death, the Omaha tribe was never again as powerful. Buffalo herds, the major food source of the Omaha people, were being decimated. As buffalo became scarce, the Sioux raided Omaha villages to capture horses and to drive the Omaha people from their rich hunting grounds. There were continuous intrusions of Anglo Americans into the lives of the Omaha. The Omaha leaders believed that the only way they could preserve their nation was to sign the Treaty of 1854, requiring them to move to a reservation.

TWO

Economic and Cultural Dispossession

The Gradual Economic and Cultural Dispossession of the Omaha Nation

In the 1700s, the Omaha people had no concept of the changes that would occur once European explorers, fur traders, settlers, and the U.S. government became more involved in their lives.

On July 12, 1775, the Second Continental Congress legislated that they would assume control over all Native American tribes in what was to become the United States of America. This decision was not intended to have a negative effect on Native Americans. However, this action resulted in a forced confinement of many of them to reservations, including confining the Omaha tribe to the Macy Reservation. This decision also resulted in hundreds of years of fighting between Native Americans and whites and heartbreak that ended the Native American way of life as they knew it.

The Louisiana Purchase

In 1803, U.S. President Thomas Jefferson purchased over 500 million acres of land from Napoleon Bonaparte of France for fifteen million dollars. Despite rules for "occupancy and use," the conquering nations of Europe never recognized indigenous ownership of American land. Thus, France acquired the Louisiana Territory from Spain and sold the land to the U.S., even though none of the countries had a basis for occupying this territory.

This land, the "Louisiana Territory," extended from the Mississippi River to the Rocky Mountains, and from Canada to the Gulf of Mexico. Jefferson requested that Meriwether Lewis and William Clark and their party travel to the territory and provide him reassurance that he had made a good decision when he purchased the land. Jefferson discovered that he had made a tremendous bargain. The territory was found to contain rich mineral resources, productive soil, multiple forests, valuable grazing land, herds of buffalo for food and hunting, and an enormous variety of other plant and animal life. With the purchase, the size of the United States doubled.[1] The states of Missouri, Arkansas, Iowa, South Dakota, and Nebraska were entirely within the Louisiana Territory. Also, within the territory were parts of Louisiana, Kansas, Colorado, Wyoming, Montana, Minnesota, North Dakota, and Oklahoma. The Louisiana Purchase is still considered the greatest land acquisition in U.S. history.

The Lewis and Clark Expedition

Meriweather Lewis and William Clark
In 1804. led an expedition exploring the Louisiana Territory at the request of President Thomas Jefferson Nebraska State Historical Society Photographic Collections.

Twenty-nine-year-old Meriwether Lewis was private secretary to Jefferson and was chosen to lead an expedition to explore the new territory. Lewis asked his friend, thirty-three-year-old William Clark, to join him in heading the expedition, and the U.S. Congress awarded them $2500 for their exploration. President Jefferson wanted a map of the safest and swiftest route through the western territory to the Pacific Ocean. Lewis and Clark were also to keep a journal throughout their expedition, and they were to record the lands, plants, animals, and humans they encountered. A Native American woman named Sacagawea was one of the guides assisting the expedition, and she was the first indigenous woman in U.S. history to be documented in a journal. The journey began on May 14, 1804, and records were kept in the journal for over twenty-eight months.

For the most part, all the interactions between Native Americans and Lewis and Clark during the expedition were peaceful. The journals they kept contained multiple pages of information about the tribes they encountered. They documented that on one occasion, when visiting a Sioux camp, they encountered forty members of the Omaha tribe captured by the Sioux. During their journey, they also visited the gravesite of the Omaha Chief, Blackbird. These journals were the first time the white population in the east were introduced to the Omaha tribal people. The Lewis and Clark Journals no doubt hastened the migration of white settlers in the east to the great unknowns in the frontier west. It has been said that the Lewis and Clark Expedition heralded the beginning of the end of the Native American way of life.

Francis La Flesche wrote the following in his book *The Middle Five*:

> *The white people speak of the country . . . as a wilderness . . . without human interest or history. To us Indians it was as clearly defined then as it is today; we knew the boundaries of tribal lands, those of our friends and those of our foes; we were familiar with every stream, the contour of every hill . . . It was our home, the scene of our history, and we loved it as our country.*[2]

Although President Jefferson encouraged Lewis and Clark to maintain peaceful and cooperative relations with the Native Americans, Jefferson's personal views about Native Americans were the opposite. In secret meetings and private letters, Jefferson stated that he wanted the new territory to be populated by educated citizen-farmers.[3] He was strongly opposed to the Native American way of life, believing that they should either become a part of the Anglo-American culture or should be removed from their homelands, with the use of force if necessary. Jefferson's views marked the beginning of one hundred years of government policy that pressured Native Americans to reform and assimilate to the white culture and ended with their forced confinement to reservations.

Our forefathers, as well as U.S. presidents in the 1700s and the 1800s, believed that their first responsibility as leaders was to build and preserve a nation united in purpose. They believed that all Americans, from the Atlantic to the Pacific, should be loyal to one government and one flag. They were concerned that Native Americans were fiercely loyal to their tribes and not to the white nation. Thus, to survive in America, Native Americans should assimilate to the dominant white culture. That meant speaking the English language and practicing white customs and traditions. Tribal leaders recognized that they needed to interact with white America to survive. They also fought aggressively to preserve their language, traditions, and sacred beliefs.

The U.S. Treaty of 1854:[4] *Confinement to a Reservation*

Throughout history, two of the greatest chiefs of the Omaha tribe were Chief Blackbird and Chief Big Elk. Of the two leaders, Big Elk was more diplomatic, more thoughtful, and he was determined to lead his people into the future.[5] In 1837, Big Elk visited Washington, D.C., as a guest of the U.S government. He saw for himself the huge flood of whites[6] in the cities and predicted they would soon be moving west to the Nebraska Territory. After his visit, he called the Omaha people together and warned them of the overwhelming changes to come due to the influx of white settlers. He also warned them about more frequent attacks by the Sioux tribe, as the Sioux were needing horses and supplies to defend against the Anglo Americans. Big Elk appointed his foster son, Joseph La Flesche, as the chief to succeed him. Of all the tribal people, he believed that Joseph La Flesche would be most able to interact with the white culture.

Big Elk (1770-1846).
Great Chief and leader of Omaha Indians. Adopted Joseph La Flesche and designated him as successor. Courtesy of Smithsonian.

By the mid-1800s, there were an increasing number of skirmishes between the Plains tribes and the white settlers. Both the leaders of the Plains tribes and the U.S. government agreed that having white settlers and tribes sharing the same lands had become untenable. Joseph La Flesche was also fearful of the increasing number of attacks on his people by the Sioux.

Thus, Joseph La Flesche accompanied the leaders of eight other Plains tribes to Washington, D.C., in 1853 on a mission of peace. As a result of the peace treaty (the Treaty of 1854) that was signed on this mission, the Omaha people agreed to move to a reservation in northeast Nebraska. From the 1700s to 1853, the Omaha tribe had claimed one-third of the present state of Nebraska as their land. By signing this peace treaty, the Omaha gave up over five million acres of land in return for a reservation of 302,000 acres. The tribe was given one year to arrange their affairs and move to the reservation. The reservation was named the "Macy" Reservation; the name Macy was formed by merging the words "Omaha" and "Agency."

Logan Fontanelle (1825–1855)
Nebraska State Historical Society Photographic Collections.

Logan Fontanelle. The interpreter during the 1853–1854 negotiations between the Plains tribal leaders and the U.S. government was Logan Fontanelle (1825–1855). Fontanelle was the grandson of Big Elk, his mother was the daughter of Big Elk, and his father was a respected French American fur trader. Fontanelle was chosen to attend the negotiations because he could speak and read perfect English, and he could interpret words and writings to the chiefs at the negotiation. He had been interpreter at the Bellevue "Indian" Agency in Nebraska for many years and was an ally of Joseph La Flesche.

According to government documents, U.S. leaders considered Fontanelle, and not Joseph La Flesche, the Chief of the Omaha tribe from 1853 to 1855. However, from 1853 to 1855, the Omaha people identified Joseph La Flesche as their Chief. Due to Fontanelle's personal effort and natural ability, he later did attain prestige among the Omaha people. Fontanelle died in a battle in 1855. Thus, beginning in 1855, there was no controversy about Joseph La Flesche's position as Omaha Chief.

In 1855, at the age of thirty, while taking part in an Omaha tribe summer buffalo hunt, Fontanelle was murdered and scalped by the Sioux.[7] Chief Joseph La Flesche and the other Omaha warriors participating in the hunt proclaimed Fontanelle a hero for his participation in the battle. After the battle, and because of his other contributions to the Omaha, Fontanelle was honored both by the Omaha people and by the white culture. Places in Omaha, Nebraska, that have been named in his honor include Hotel Fontanelle, Fontanelle Boulevard, and several elementary and middle schools. Fontanelle Forest in Bellevue, Nebraska, is a major attraction for citizens of Bellevue and Omaha.

According to the Treaty of 1854, the United States agreed to pay the Omaha tribe sums of money for the large amount of land they were losing. The tribe was to receive forty thousand dollars annually for the next three years, thirty thousand dollars annually for the following ten years, and twenty thousand dollars annually for the fifteen years after. At his discretion, the U.S. President could provide buildings and fencing, food, stock, merchandise, and medical care in place of part or all the annual sums of money.

Additionally, in return for receiving the land, the US. agreed to erect for the tribe a grist and sawmill; to provide a miller for the sawmill for ten years; to erect a quality blacksmith shop supplied with tools and to keep it in repair for ten years; and to provide a quality blacksmith for the shop for ten years. The government recognized that the Omaha people had little experience in farming and agreed to employ an experienced farmer for ten years to teach them about agriculture. The U.S. also agreed to protect the Omaha people on the reservation from the Sioux and all other hostile tribes. The Omaha people were to promise to be friendly to their white neighbors, and to not make war on any other tribe, except in self-defense.

At the time the tribe moved to the reservation, Chief Joseph La Flesche proposed strict regulations to prevent alcohol abuse on the reservation. He assigned a police force of thirty men to maintain order on the reservation and to arrest any drunken tribal member. This regulation on the use of alcohol persisted until Joseph La Flesche's death in 1888.[8]

By signing the 1854 treaty, the Omaha tribe lost a large amount of land. At the time, signing the treaty appeared to be the best solution to the constant skirmishes between the Omaha people and the white settlers. The treaty appeared to meet the needs of both the Omaha tribe and the U.S. Government. The reservation system allowed the tribe to have legal ownership of land, provided protection from their enemies, and gave the Omaha people the right to govern themselves.

Unfortunately, as with many of the other treaties and promises they had made, the U.S. government did not uphold their part of the agreement. Often the Omaha people were left wanting for supplies, annuities, and cash. The government had promised to provide food, livestock, and other supplies as needed to the people on the reservation; however, supplies were often delivered late, or not at all. The sawmill "blew up" three months after it was built and was not repaired until three years later. Although the government had promised assistance to the Omaha people in developing their land and protecting them from their enemies, they did not receive such assistance. One major reason for the government's failure to keep its promises was that the "Indian" agents assigned to the reservation were corrupt. *"Politics, greed, and corruption combined to create controversy during the Omahas' early reservation period. Agents seldom remained for long; many were inept or dictatorial, and at least one, Agent J.B. Robertson, proved to be dishonest."*[9]

The following is a map of the location of the Native American tribes in Nebraska following the Omaha people's move to the reservation.

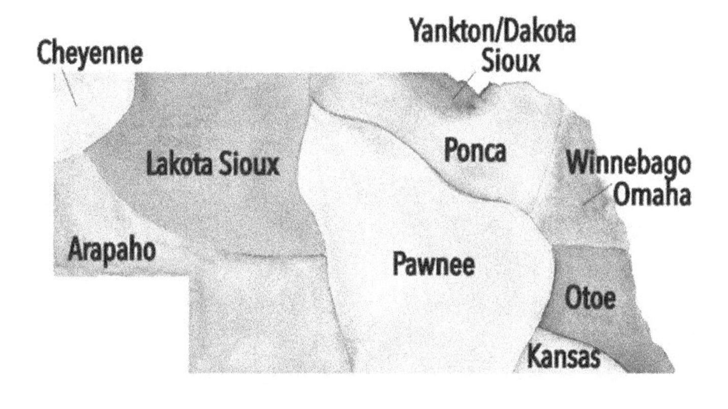

Native American Tribes in the Nebraska Territory in the 1800's.
Illustration by Erica Parker Rogers.

In the 1860s, the Nebraska Territory consisted of ten Indian tribes: the Cheyenne, Arapahoe, Lakota Sioux, Yankton/Dakota Sioux, Ponca, Pawnee, Kansas, Otoe, Winnebago, and Omaha, and locations for tribal areas are approximate. The Omaha engaged in intermittent warfare with the Dakota and Lakota Sioux, Cheyenne, and Otoe tribes. Today, the

U.S. government recognizes the following six tribes in Nebraska: the Iowa Tribe, the Omaha Tribe, the Ponca Tribe, the Sac & Fox Nation, the Santee Sioux Tribe, and the Winnebago Tribe.

Many of the Omaha people did continue their nomadic lifestyles and buffalo hunts even after their move to the reservation. However, by 1870, their traditional lifestyle had been virtually abandoned. Two occurrences at the end of the 1800s hastened the demise of the buffalo and the flood of white settlers in Nebraska: the passing of the Homestead Act in 1862, and the completion of the Transcontinental Railroad in 1869.

The Homestead Act of 1862.

The Homestead Act was signed by Abraham Lincoln on May 20,1862 and went into effect on January 1, 1863. Leading advocates for the Homestead Act included Horace Greeley, who coined the phrase "Go West, Young Man," and George Henry Evans, who introduced the slogan "Vote Yourself a Farm."

The Act provided 160 acres of free public land to white (not Native American) settlers who agreed to pay a fourteen-dollar fee, to develop and improve the land, and to reside on the land for at least five years. The Act was intended to make land available to soldiers who had fought in the Civil War, to recently freed slaves from the south, and to independent farmers who could otherwise not afford the land.

Not all farmers were able to take advantage of the Homestead Act because they could not afford the tools, seed, and livestock necessary to improve the land. However, over eighty million acres of land were distributed by the government because of the Act. The first settler to claim 160 acres of land was Daniel Freeman, a Civil War veteran. He built his home on land that is now a part of Gage County, Nebraska, near the city of Beatrice. The site of his claim is now the Homestead National Park.

As a result of the Homestead Act, an increased number of white settlers came to the Nebraska Territory. White traders and buffalo hunters came with these settlers, and buffalo herds began to diminish.

Completion of the Transcontinental Railroad—1869

On May 10, 1869, the Central Pacific Railroad's tracks from the west were connected to the Union Pacific Railroad's tracks from the east in Promontory Summit, Utah. The completion of the Transcontinental Railroad is recognized as one of the United States' biggest achievements and one of mankind's greatest accomplishments. The United States became unified. The Transcontinental Railroad reduced travel time from New York to California from as long as six months to as little as a week, and the result was an even greater migration to the west. The expansion dramatically increased the wealth of America.

Completion of the transcontinental railroad—May 10, 1869
Central Pacific Railroad's tracks from the west were connected to Union Pacific Railroad's tracks from the east at Promontory Summit, Utah. Shuttlestock.

Demise of the Buffalo

The railroad was also a major cause of the decimation of the buffalo.[10] Massive hunting parties began to arrive in the west by train, with thousands of men packing .50 caliber rifles, and leaving a trail of buffalo carnage in their wake. Buffaloes were easily located and killed, and buffalo hides were valuable in the east. Even buffalo bones were sold, ground, and used as a fertilizer. In the 1800s, it was estimated that fur traders often killed 100 buffalos every hour. Over 200,000 buffalo were killed annually. Hunting parties generally left buffalo meat and carcasses on the prairie to rot.

U.S. policy condoned and may have even encouraged the slaughter of the buffalo. Some U.S. leaders believed that killing buffalo was one way of eliminating the "Indian problem." Prior to the 1800s, there were millions of buffalo roaming the plains, and the Omaha people could hunt enough buffalo to keep them fed and warm. By the end of the 1800s, the buffalo almost all but vanished. There were less than one thousand buffalo roaming the plains and available for hunting. Historically, every summer, the Omaha people participated in "buffalo hunts." Buffalo hunts came to an end in the 1870s and 1880s.[11]

Plains Wars of the post-Civil War Era

The U.S. government was determined to move all Native Americans to reservations, by force if necessary. As a result of the demise of the buffalo and forced confinement to the reservations, there was brutal fighting between the American government and many of the Native American tribes.

The year 1870 has been considered the beginning of the worst years of warfare with the Plains Native American tribes. The five tribes most feared by the U.S. army were the Comanches,[12] Apaches,[13] Cheyenne,[14] Kiowa,[15], and Sioux.[16] The Comanches, led by Quanah Parker, engaged in warfare with the whites in Texas and Oklahoma. They were war-like and aggressive, and for over twenty years both the Texas Militia and the Mexican government were unable to contain them. The Kiowas, led by Satanta, often accompanied the Comanches on their raids. The Apaches, led by Geronimo and Cochise, were fierce warriors and skillful tacticians who fought the U.S. Army before and after the Civil War. They lived in the Arizona and New Mexico regions, and during the Civil War were feared both by the Confederate and Union soldiers. The Cheyenne tribe lived in the Rocky Mountain and Southern Montana area, and members of the tribe were extremely disruptive to Colorado ranchers. The ranchers fought with heavily armed militia. The Cheyenne warriors on horseback, called "dog soldiers" were known for their persistence, regardless of the size of militia against them. The Sioux tribe, with their leader Sitting Bull, are famously known for defeating the U.S. 7th Cavalry at the Battle of Little Bighorn.

Warren Wagon Train Raid or Salt Creek Massacre.[17] There were two conflicts during this post-Civil War period that angered the U.S. government to such an extent that they talked openly about eliminating all Native Americans, regardless of their tribe. The first was called the "Warren Wagon Train Raid" on May 18, 1871. Henry Warren was contracted to haul supplies to forts in the west of Texas, including Fort Richardson, Fort Griffin, and Fort Concho. The wagon train consisted of ten mule drawn wagons filled with food and supplies and was travelling down the Jacksboro-Belknap-Road leading toward Salt Creek Crossing. At one point on the trail, the wagon train and muleskinners were greeted by General William Sherman. Soon after, the wagons were attacked by the Kiowa tribe, led by Satanta (White Bear).[18] All the food and supplies were either destroyed or taken from the wagons, and seven of the muleskinners were killed. One of these seven had been tortured to death with fire and his tongue had been cut out. Five muleskinners survived. After this incident, General Sherman became obsessed with capturing Satanta and his band of Kiowa. Satanta was eventually captured at Fort Sill and convicted of murder.

Battle of Little Bighorn.[19] A second battle occurred on June 25 and 26,1876, and involved the Sioux tribe led by Sitting Bull[20] and Crazy Horse. History has since referred to this as the "Battle of the Little Bighorn" or "Custer's Last Stand." In the second treaty of Fort Laramie, the U.S. government guaranteed that the Sioux and Arapahoe had possession of the Dakota Territory—the land west of the Missouri River. However, the U.S. broke the treaty and went to war with the Sioux over the land.

Thus, the 7th Cavalry, led by Lieutenant Colonel George Armstrong Custer, was assigned to battle the Lakota Sioux. The fight took place in Southern Montana, near the Little Bighorn River. The 7th Cavalry, consisting of 700 men in 12 companies, suffered a major defeat. Five companies were wiped out, and casualties included Custer, two of his brothers, a nephew, and a brother-in-law. The U.S. casualty count included 274 dead and 49 wounded. This defeat is often considered the worst defeat ever suffered by the U.S. Cavalry.

Sitting Bull (1831–1890)
Courtesy of Smithsonian.

George Armstrong Custer (1839–1876)
Courtesy of Smithsonian.

After the battle, Custer was considered by many to be a heroic figure. However, other historians have questioned his decision-making during the battle. According to historians, Custer had been misinformed about the number of Sioux he would be fighting. He believed the number would be less than 800. There were over 2000 Sioux. Instead of attacking them with a full force of twelve companies, Custer divided the twelve companies into smaller groups. Custer led five of the companies, and Major Marcus Reno and Captain Frederick Benteen led the other companies. This was a grave mistake because Custer and his five companies fought in the battle alone. In the confusion, Reno and Benteen's companies were not able to help Custer.

These five tribes, the Comanche, Apache, Cheyenne, Kiowa, and Sioux were involved in deadly battles with the U.S. Cavalry. However, their anger and brutality were often related to their loss of land, forced confinement to reservations, and the U.S. breaking treaties. Also, not all Native American tribes were involved in battles against the U.S. Yet, in the end, most Native Americans, including the Omaha tribe, were treated the same way by our U.S. government.

Brigadier General Crook was one of many who recognized the tragedy of Native American tribes having "no rights" under the law. Peaceful tribes like the Omaha, who never once took up arms against the U.S. government, were never listened to by the government. The only tribes who commanded any respect were the ones who inspired terror with their rifles.

Partially resulting from these "post-Civil War" battles with the Plains tribes, armies were given more punitive powers. President Ulysses Grant and former Union army generals such as William Sherman and Phil Sheridan encouraged U.S. policies that would eliminate the "problem of Indians."

In later years, Sheridan did express some regret for his role in destroying buffalo herds and the loss of livelihood for Native Americans. In his *Annual Report of the General of the U.S. Army: 1878,* Sheridan acknowledged that Native Americans were forced onto reservations with no compensation beyond the promise of basic supplies of food and clothing—promises, he wrote, which were never fulfilled.

Sheridan wrote in his report: "*We took away their country and their means of support, broke up their mode of living, their habits of life, introduced disease and decay among them, and it was for this and against this that they made war. Could anyone expect less? Then, why wonder at Indian difficulties.*"[21]

Although Sheridan and other Americans did appear sympathetic to Native Americans, another report, the *Report of the United States Commissioner for Indian Affairs (1881)*, included the following statement: "*Savage and civilized life cannot live and prosper on the same ground. One of the two must die.*"[22]

The Dawes or "Allotment" Act of 1887

The Dawes Act of 1887 was legislated in part to respond to Anglo American ranchers and farmers who were petitioning the government to get access to the reservation lands. There was the perception that the reservation lands were fertile ground for crops and livestock and were not being fully used. Lawmakers like Senator Henry Dawes of Massachusetts wanted to ensure that the Omaha people would not lose their land. In 1891, he was quoted as saying: *"I never knew a white man who had his foot on an Indian's land who ever took it off."*[23]

Senator Dawes also believed that Native Americans would progress further if they lost their traditions, their identities, and their tribalism and became more "Euro-Americanized." Thus, in 1887, Congress enacted the "General Allotment" or "Dawes" Act.[24] The purpose of the Act was to distribute the reservation land among individual tribal members with the aim of creating responsible farmers in the white man's image. The intent of the Dawes Act was to achieve the following goals: a) to break up tribes as social units; b) to encourage individual initiatives; c) to further the progress of Native American farmers; d) to reduce the cost of administration of reservations; e) to secure parts of the reservations as Native American land; and f) to open the remainder of the land to white settlers for profit. Heads of families were to receive a grant of 160 acres on the reservation that would be designated as "their" land.

Senator Dawes and U.S. legislatures believed that the laws they were passing would benefit the Omaha tribe and all Native American tribes. Generally, the opposite was true, The Dawes Act was meant to encourage individual ownership of land. However, legislators totally ignored the fact that most Omaha people knew little English, were not able to read or understand deeds, and had no desire to become farmers.

Many tribal members sold their lots to the white settlers for very little money. The result was that Native Americans lost even more land due to the Dawes Act. Nationally, between 1887 and 1934, due of this Act, tribal members lost control of about two-thirds of the land base they held in 1887. The loss of land and break-up of traditional leadership of tribes produced negative cultural and social effects that have since prompted scholars to refer to the Dawes Act as one of the most destructive U.S. policies for Native Americans in history.

> *The irony and tragedy of the Omaha story is that this small peace-loving Indian tribe, whose progressive leaders truly wanted to "walk the white man's road," were led partly down that road and then were*

expected to continue their own, without the necessary skills or resources to survive in the world that had been created for them.[25]

Malnutrition, Sickness, and Depression on the Reservation

In the seventeenth and eighteenth centuries, prior to the introduction of infectious diseases, Omaha people were for the most part physically fit. Although surviving was not easy, most of the time they had adequate food and were active at work and play. Due to accidents and warfare, they did have arrow wounds, cuts (often severe), bruises, muscle strain, broken bones, and animal bites. Elderly Omaha people suffered from diseases of aging, such as rheumatism and arthritis. Joint stiffness and pain were especially a problem in the elderly when they slept on blankets over the high terrain. Prior to life on the reservation, the Omaha people were nomads who lived in small tribal clans. They lived near rivers or lakes, and they used water for drinking and bathing that was not contaminated by "germs." They moved frequently; thus, there were not large buildups of sewage and waste products near their earth homes and tipis. Thus, they were somewhat protected against the development and spread of infectious diseases.

From the 1860s to the 1880s, Omaha people who had been moved to the reservation and who no longer had buffalo to hunt suffered from malnutrition and were haunted by diseases such as influenza, tuberculosis, measles, and dysentery, and occasionally typhoid fever and even cholera. Susan La Flesche wrote of the many people on the reservation who were both discouraged and depressed. She was also concerned early on that the Omaha people had an unusual reaction to and fondness for alcohol.

Omaha people on the reservation lacked adequate access to medical care. Although white agency doctors had been assigned to care for them, some of the doctors had little regard for Native Americans and spent little time providing them care. The following paragraph describes an incident on the reservation when Susan was a child.

When Susan La Flesche was a young girl on the Macy reservation, she went to help care for a sick elderly Omaha woman who was on a blanket in a buckskin tipi. She was feverish and in agony. Susan fed her broth and tried to cool her with a wet cloth. Finally, the elderly woman fainted. Four times during the night, a messenger was sent to tell the white agency doctor that his help was needed to care for the woman. Four times during the night, the doctor promised he would soon be there. But he never came, and the woman died an agonizing death. [26]

Later, it was discovered that the doctor hunted prairie chickens instead of caring for the women. Susan decided that if she were a doctor, she would respond quickly to the Omaha people in need of medical care because their lives mattered to her.

Before the time of Susan La Flesche, tribal members were distrustful of the white agency doctors. Doctors could not be counted on to come when they were needed, and Omaha people also believed that many of their diseases came from Anglo Americans. Most Omaha people, when they were sick, died without ever seeing a doctor. This changed when Dr. Susan La Flesche, who was also a member of the Omaha tribe, returned to the reservation in 1889 to practice medicine. Susan spoke the Omaha language, knew their customs and traditions, and she cared about her patients. The Omaha people readily accepted her as their doctor.

THREE

Dr. Susan La Flesche Picotte

Enter Susan La Flesche.

In 1865, Susan La Flesche was born in a tipi on the Macy reservation. In 1889, at the age of twenty-four, she graduated from the Women's Medical College in Philadelphia, Pennsylvania. "*On March 14, 1889, Susan La Flesche Picotte received her medical degree, becoming the first Native American doctor in U.S. history—thirty-one years before women could vote and thirty-five years before Native Americans could become citizens in their own country.*"[1] Susan was a small woman and somewhat frail, and she died in 1915 at the relatively early age of fifty. Yet, she led an incredible life, providing medical care and advocating for her tribe of Omaha people for over a quarter of a century. Susan's accomplishments, generosity, and dedication to the Omaha people were influenced by the words and wisdom of her parents.

Susan's father was Joseph La Flesche, Chief of the Omaha tribe. Joseph's father was a wealthy white French fur trader, and Joseph's mother was a member of the Ponca tribe of Native Americans. Young Joseph La Flesche lived in two worlds. He learned both the French language and culture from his father, and the Ponca tribal language and culture from his mother.[2]

Susan's mother was Mary Gale,[3] and she was also a child of mixed blood. Mary's father was a white U. S. Army Surgeon, and her mother was a Native American and member of the Ioway tribe. Mary Gale was also reported to be a relative of the Omaha chief, Chief Big Elk. After years of trading with the Omaha tribe, young Joseph was adopted as a son of Chief Big Elk, and later, he succeeded Big Elk as chief.

The Joseph La Flesch family were considered "prominent and affluent" members of the Omaha tribe. Joseph was described as a man of integrity and intelligence. He recognized that Anglo Americans were in Nebraska to stay, and there was much about the white culture to be admired. During his time as Chief, Joseph or "Iron Eye" tried to show the Indian people how they could retain the best parts of their culture and still succeed in the white man's world. He believed his people's future would lie in education and in interacting with the white culture, including the adoption of the white man's agriculture. He believed that both men and women should seek higher education, and that both could become leaders in their community. He encouraged all his children to seek a lifetime career that involved service to others. He was quoted as saying: "*My dear young daughters, do you want to simply be called those Indians, or do you want to go to school and be somebody in the world?*"[4]

The Two Families of Joseph La Flesche—Francis, Rosalie, Marguerite, Susette, and Susan

It was common practice in the 1800s for tribal chiefs to have two wives.[5] Joseph's wives were Mary Gale and Elizabeth Esau. Joseph had five children with Mary Gale—a son named Louis, who died at the age of twelve, and four daughters: Susette, Rosalie, Marguerite, and Susan. He had three children with his wife Elizabeth Esau—two sons named Francis and Carey and a daughter, Lucy. Five of his children are recognized today as prominent leaders in Nebraska history—Rosalie, Marguerite, Francis, Susette, and Susan.

The Two Families of Joseph La Flesche

1. Joseph La Flesche, 1822–1889	**Mary Gale 1826–1907**
Children:	
Louis 1848–1860	
Susette 1854–1903	—T.H. Tibbles
Rosalie 1861–1900	—Edward Farley (3 girls 7 boys)
Marguerite 1862–1945	—Charles Picotte
	—Walter T. Diddock (2 girls 3 boys)
Susan 1865–1915	—Henry Picotte (2 boys)

2. Joseph La Flesche, 1822–1889	**Elizabeth Esau Died 1883**
Children:	
Francis 1857–1932	—Alice Mitchell (Divorced}
	—Rosa Bourassa (Separated)
Lucy 1865–1923	—Noah (Leaming) La Flesche
Carey 1872–1952	—Phoebe Cline (4 girls 2 boys)

Father—Joseph La Flesche, Jr. (1822–1889) Chief of the Omaha tribe. *Believed in the importance of education for Native Americans, and in interacting with the white culture. Nebraska State Historical Society Photographic Collections.*

Mother—Mary Gale (1826–1907) *First wife of Joseph La Flesche. Mother of Susan La Flesche. Nebraska State Historical Society Photographic Collections.*

Sister—Rosalie La Flesche Farley (1861–1900) *Taught at Mission School and was business manager for the Omaha tribe. Advocated for the right of autonomy for Native Americans. Nebraska State Historical Society Photographic Collections.*

Sister—Marguerite La Flesche Picotte Diddock (1862–1945) *Taught at Omaha Indian school and worked to establish libraries on the reservation. Nebraska State Historical Society Photographic Collections.*

Half-Brother—Francis La Flesche (1857–1932) *Son of Joseph La Flesche and Elizabeth Esau. First Native American anthropologist in the U.S. Nebraska State Historical Society Photographic Collections.*

Sister—Susette La Flesche Tibbles (1854–1903) *Eulogized as first woman to speak out for the cause of Native Americans. Nebraska State Historical Society Photographic Collections.*

Susette's husband—Thomas Tibbles
Assistant Editor of Omaha Daily Herald Nebraska State Historical Society Photographic Collections.

Susan La Flesche Picotte (1865–1900) *Provider of medical care and advocate for the Omaha tribe of NE from 1890 to 1915. Nebraska State Historical Society Photographic Collections.*

Sons of Susan and Henry Picotte— Caryl and Pierre Picotte.
Nebraska State Historical Society Photographic Collections.

Only known picture of Susan's husband—Henry Picotte
Far left is Susan La Flesche, next is sister Marguerite and her husband, Walter Diddock. Seated is Henry Picotte. Courtesy of Hampton University Archives.

Susan's sister Rosalie married Edward Farley, and their marriage produced ten children. Both Rosalie and Edward taught at the Mission School on the reservation. Rosalie also acted as a business manager for the Omaha tribe and helped with financial affairs. Rosalie was especially admired and respected by the tribe because she advocated for self-government on the reservation. The Anglo Americans wanted the Native Americans to "assimilate" to their white culture. Rosalee advocated for the Omaha people to interact with Anglo Americans but also to remain autonomous. The village of Rosalie in Nebraska was named as a tribute to Rosalie La Flesche Farley.

Marguerite La Flesche was highly educated (both at the Elizabeth Institute in New Jersey and at the Hampton Institute in Virginia). Her first marriage was to Charles Picotte, a Native American from the Sioux tribe, and Charles died several years into the marriage of tuberculosis. She later married a white American, Walter Diddock, and they had five children. Marguerite taught for many years at the Omaha Agency Government school in Nebraska, and later became a field officer at the Office of Indian Affairs (OIA). At that time, she was directed by the OIA to use any means necessary to accelerate the adoption of Euro-American culture within the Omaha community. This "assimilation" of Native Americans to the white culture was opposed by her own sister, Rosalie. Marguerite made many important contributions to the Omaha tribe. She worked to establish libraries on the reservation,[6] and she also served on the election board after the 19th amendment passed. The 19th amendment awarded Omaha people the right to vote.

Susan's half-brother, Francis La Flesche, was the son of Joseph and his wife, Elizabeth Esau. Francis was credited as being the first Native American anthropologist in the U.S. He earned undergraduate and master's degrees at George Washington University Law School in Washington, D.C., and worked at the Smithsonian Institution. One of Francis's most famous works is a memoir written in 1900 entitled "*The Middle Five: Indian Boys at School*," and the memoir described his experiences as a student at a Presbyterian Mission Boarding school on the reservation. Francis also collaborated with Alice Cunningham Fletcher in 1911 in authoring a book entitled "*The Omaha Tribe*." Francis lived in Washington, D.C., and among Anglo Americans for most of his life. In 1922, he was elected a member of the National Academy of Sciences. In 1923, he was elected as president of the Anthropological Society of Washington, and in 1926, he was awarded an Honorary Doctor of Letters by the University of Nebraska. When Francis died in 1932, he asked to be buried in Bancroft, Nebraska, near the graves of his father and half-sister Susette.

Susan's older sister, Susette, was well-known nationally as a champion of Native American rights.[7] Susette was also called "*Inshata Theumba*" or "bright eyes."[8] In 1882, Susette married Thomas Tibbles, the assistant editor of the *Omaha Daily Herald*. Susette was a prolific writer for the newspaper. She also played an important role in two incidents involving the U.S. government and Native Americans, and both incidents have had major historical implications. "The Trial of Standing Bear" and the "Massacre at Wounded Knee" are described in the following paragraphs.

The Trial of Standing Bear—1887

Standing Bear[9] was one of the chiefs of the Ponca tribe, located at the Niobrara River Valley in Nebraska—north of the Omaha tribe and south and east of the Sioux reservation. In 1868, General William Sherman signed the Treaty of Fort Laramie, illegally giving the Ponca reservation to Red Cloud and the Sioux. The treaty was signed to end the numerous wars with the Sioux.

The story of Standing Bear begins in 1877 when, as required by the treaty, the Ponca tribe was forced to leave their home in Nebraska and move to the Indian Territory in Oklahoma, 800 miles away. Soldiers rounded up the people of the tribe and helped them to get their wagons ready and begin their travel to the south. The Poncas walked 600 miles to the new territory, and the journey took fifty-five days—from May 16 to July 9, 1877. Reports are that one-third of the tribe died, either during the dreaded walk or in the first years living at the Oklahoma reservation. Standing Bear's granddaughter, Prairie Flower, died along the journey as well as many others.

The Ponca tribe struggled in the new reservation. When they arrived in Oklahoma, there was no one to meet them. The Ponca people found that the U.S. government had neglected to provide for them even minimal housing, clothing, food, water, farming equipment, and medicine. The results were persistent famine. By the spring of 1878, there were multiple deaths, due to starvation, malaria, and other infectious diseases. Standing Bear wrote numerous letters to the U.S. president or "Great Father" telling him that the Ponca wanted to go home to Nebraska. His letters were never answered.

Susette La Flesche Tibbles was outraged when the Poncas were forced to move to Oklahoma. Even the white settlers who lived nearby and supposedly hated the Poncas opposed them being taken away by force. One spring, Susette travelled by train and stagecoach to visit the Poncas in Oklahoma. She was shocked by the malnutrition and sickness on the reservation. During the move, the Ponca had left many of their belongings at the Ponca village in Nebraska. At their former residence, they were surviving, and some had a net worth of thousands of dollars. At the Indian Territory in Oklahoma, they became beggars. The Poncas lived in unheated tents, were unable to work or plant crops, had no school, and there was sickness, including malaria, everywhere. Standing Bear's eldest son, Bear Shield, was among the Poncas who died in the new territory.

Standing Bear wanted to bury his son up north in the Niobrara River Valley in Nebraska. He and thirty of his followers returned to Nebraska to bury his son, and they were welcomed warmly by Susette La Flesche Tibbles, Thomas Tibbles, and the Omaha people at the Macy Reservation.

Unfortunately, because Standing Bear had left the reservation assigned to him, the U.S. military arrested him and planned to return him to Oklahoma. Native American reservations in the 1800s were like prisons. Tribal members were forced by the military to leave their homes and move to reservations, often hundreds of miles away. Once on the reservation they were forbidden to leave. In truth, prisons today would furnish more adequate food, supplies, and medical care than what the Native Americans received in reservations during the mid-1800s.

Both Brigadier General George Crook and Thomas Tibbles were sympathetic to the Ponca and Standing Bear and were appalled by the conditions in Oklahoma. Tibbles publicized the Ponca's story in the *Omaha Daily Herald.* Crook and Tibbles began the process of submitting a writ of *habeas corpus* that would result in a trial in the U.S. District Court in Omaha, Nebraska. They argued that Standing Bear was a person, and imprisonment of a person without just cause was illegal. The U.S. had no cause for arresting Standing Bear and for holding him in captivity. This was a landmark case because historically, Native Americans were not legally entitled to the same rights and protections as Anglo Americans.

At the trial, Standing Bear was allowed to speak on his own behalf. The following is his statement that still resonates today: "*This hand is not the color of yours, but I prick it, the blood will flow, and I shall feel pain. This blood is of the same color as yours. God made me, and I am a Man.*"[10] On May 12, 1879, Judge Elmer Dundy delivered his decision in favor of Standing Bear, that "*an Indian is a person.*" "*Indians are living souls,*[11] *self-conscious beings, moral agents, and individuals of the human race.*" Elmer Dundy has since been recognized for his courage in recognizing the worth of Native Americans. Dundy County in southwestern Nebraska has been named for Judge Dundy.

During the trial, Susette La Flesche Tibbles served as interpreter for Standing Bear. Standing Bear's message was communicated, and only a competent interpreter could make this happen. After the trial, Susette and Francis La Flesche joined Standing Bear in his travels to the eastern U.S. and Europe. At each stop, they advocated for the rights of Native Americans. Susette was the first Native American woman to enter the public speaking arena. Eventually, Standing Bear returned to his home in the Niobrara River Valley, and spent the remainder of his life in Nebraska.

Today, the federal government recognizes two tribes of Poncas, the Ponca tribe in Nebraska and the Ponca tribe in Oklahoma. The Omaha Tribe, the Iowa Tribe, the Sac & Fox Nation, the Santee Sioux Tribe, and the Winnebago Tribe all have reservations in Nebraska. The official reservation for the Ponca Tribe is in Oklahoma. Although the Ponca in Nebraska have no reservation, after the trial of Standing Bear, the federal government did allot land in Nebraska for the tribe. A 15-county delivery service area was established for the Poncas in Nebraska. The 15-county delivery area offers a broad range of health, social, educational, and cultural services for the Ponca people. The main headquarters for the service delivery area for the Ponca tribe is in Niobrara, Nebraska.

Standing Bear has received numerous honors posthumously. He was elected to the Nebraska Hall of Fame, and an elementary school in Omaha, Nebraska, and high school in Lincoln, Nebraska, have been named in his honor. The logo at the Standing Bear High School in Lincoln consists of a shield and an imprint of the face of a bear and is a tribute to Bear Shield. Bear Shield, of course, is the son of Standing Bear who had died during their first years in Oklahoma. In Nebraska, there is also a Standing Bear Lake, Memorial Bridge, Park, and Museum. Statues of Standing Bear can be found in the Statuary Hall at the U.S. Capitol and at the Centennial Mall in Lincoln, Nebraska.

In 2023, film-maker Andrew Troy will begin production on a movie entitled *"I Am a Man: The True Story of Ponca Chief Standing Bear."* The movie will be based on Joe Starita's book, *"I Am a Man: Chief Standing Bear's Journey for Justice."* Production was made possible by $6 million in grants from the state of Nebraska and the Cherokee Nation Film Office.[12]. There is some encouraging news today about living on reservations. Many Plains tribe reservations are resurging because of more economic development opportunities. More Native Americans are returning to reservations to live. At many reservations, birth rates are higher than the average for other Americans. Most importantly, today all Native Americans have the same rights in the U.S. as other Americans.

In his book, *Encyclopedia of the Great Plains Indians,* David Wishart states that today: "*Far from disappearing, Native Americans and their reservation homelands are reasserting themselves on the landscape of the Great Plains.*"[13]

Massacre at Wounded Knee—1890[14]

The second major incident involving Susette La Flesche Tibbles was the Massacre at Wounded Knee in South Dakota on December 29,1890.

Bronze Statue of Standing Bear
Sculpture located at the Centennial Mall in Lincoln, Nebraska. Created by Benjamin Victor and dedicated October 15, 2017. Chief of the Ponca Tribe who went to trial in Omaha, Nebraska, arguing that he had been imprisoned without just cause. On May 12,1879, decision at trial was that Native Americans were persons with the same rights and protections as Anglo Americans. Photo by Lou Waltman.

Wounded Knee was part of the Lakota Sioux Pine Ridge Reservation and was located four hundred miles from the Omaha (Macy) reservation. At the massacre at Wounded Knee, over 290 Lakota Sioux men, women, and children were killed by the U.S. Cavalry, and fifty more were wounded.

In the late 1880s, members of both the Omaha and Lakota Sioux tribes were experiencing starvation and disease. Both tribes had been forced to move to reservations. Along with the Omaha tribe, the Lakota Sioux had lost large pieces of their land with the Dawes or General Allotment Act of 1887. The summer had been dry, the crops were poor, and the buffalo were gone. The government was not sending the tribes the rations they had been promised and was not protecting them from the white settlers and gold seekers.

The Omaha people were known as a peace-loving tribe. However, for the Lakota Sioux, fighting had long been a way of life. Their culture had been war-like for many generations. Although the Lakota Sioux had benefited from being awarded the Ponca land in the Treaty of Fort Laramie in 1868, there continued to be skirmishes with the U.S. Cavalry.

In the 1890s, there was unrest on the Sioux reservation. The Sioux people, lacking hope for the future, began to worship a Paiute prophet named Wovoka. Wovoka was the founder of the Ghost Dance religion, and he encouraged tribal members to participate in the dance. The U.S. government heard about the Ghost Dance and the widespread dissatisfaction among the Sioux. The government believed they needed to "take action" against the Sioux and decided to take some of the Sioux chiefs into custody in order to quell this "Messiah" craze. Fourteen days before the Wounded Knee Massacre, on December 15, 1890, the Cavalry attempted to take Chief Sitting Bull into custody. He refused to be taken peacefully and was shot to death by the soldiers.

On December 29, 1890, the U.S. Cavalry soldiers entered the Sioux camp to disarm the people in the camp. There were more than five hundred U.S. soldiers and four Hotchkiss cannons surrounding the camp. When a tribal weapon was accidently discharged, the soldiers' guns and cannons exploded, and a barrage of bullets assaulted the men, women, and children at the camp. Tipis were burned, and the women and children fleeing the camp were followed by the U.S. soldiers and brutally murdered.

Susette and her husband had come to the reservation intending to write a story about the soldiers at Wounded Knee. During and after the massacre, Susette was at the side of the Lakota Sioux, attending the wounded. She saw first-hand the widespread destruction at the camp. There were gunshot wounds in the bodies of Sioux women, babies, and children. During the remaining years of her life, Susette would never forget the blood and the suffering—the gruesome sights of the wounded and dead bodies—at Wounded Knee.

The Massacre at Wounded knee signaled the end of the Plains Indian Wars, and eventually, the Ghost Dance religion was no longer practiced. The Wounded Knee Battlefield, site of the massacre, has now been designated as a National Historic Landmark by the U.S. Department of the Interior. In 1990, both houses of the U.S. Congress passed a resolution on the historical centennial of the massacre, formally expressing their regret.

Susette died in 1903 at the age of forty-nine and was eulogized in the U.S. Senate as the first woman to speak out for the cause of Native Americans. In 1983, Susette was inducted into the Nebraska Hall of Fame, and in 1984, she was inducted into the National Women's Hall of Fame.

Susan La Flesche—The Early Years

Susan was the first Native American physician in the U.S., and she chose to return to her home on the reservation to practice medicine. She was especially loved by so many because she chose to work as a doctor when there were so few medical therapies available for her Omaha people, and when they were in such dire need of her help. Susan was a frail woman, and yet she chose a profession that was both emotionally and physically wearing. With little consideration for her own needs and welfare, she resolved: "*to serve others, to visit the poor, and to help the suffering humanity.*"[15]

Education at the Mission and Boarding School. As a child, Susan, along with her siblings, attended both the Presbyterian Mission School and the Omaha Agency School. Students were only allowed to speak English in the school, they were to avoid Native American cultural practices, and the boys were told to wear white man's clothes. Students in the school were called by white people's names because their tribal names were "too difficult to pronounce." Susan loved education and learning. She also had been taught by her father the importance of education. The teachers' methods of interacting with the Native American children were painful for many of the children and their families, however. According to the "theory of historical trauma," not allowing children to practice their language and cultural traditions can result in children suffering feelings of loss, lack of self-confidence, and depression.

Preparing to be a Physician—Medical Education in the 1880s. After boarding school, Susan attended the Hampton Institute in Virginia, a school for Native and African Americans, and she studied at the school for three years. After graduating from the Hampton Institute, she returned to Nebraska and worked for two years as a teacher at the Mission School on the reservation. Her goal was always to practice medicine, however. During her childhood, Susan had become interested in medicine, and she spent days watching the traditional tribal healers and the government doctor at work.

In the white man's world of 1800, American women typically did not become doctors. However, In the Omaha tribe, women often took on the role of "healer." Susan's desire to become a medical doctor was influenced by the fact that Native Americans believed that the "Great Spirit" worked equally through both men and women. Often in tribes, women healers were more likely to administer herbal and root treatments than men. Both men and women could obtain the position of shaman, and shamans were considered to have visions of the future and to have mystical powers to heal.

In the U.S. in 1886, women were excluded from most of the existing universities and medical schools. U.S. men believed that women were not equal to them in intellectual and artistic achievement, just as they believed that indigenous people were not equal to Anglo Americans. In 1869, Harriet Beecher Stowe was quoted as saying "The position of a married woman was similar to that of the slave.[16] They could not vote, they did not hold a public office, and they were given access to few jobs beyond dealing with the personal care needs of children, the sick, and the elderly.

Middle- and upper-class women did not work outside of the home. They were expected to care for their home, their husband, and their children, and to engage in charitable works.[17]

The first American woman in history to graduate from a medical school was Elizabeth Blackwell in 1849. Her entrance into medical school was not well accepted by faculty or students, and initially she was forbidden to participate in any classroom discussions or medical demonstrations. In 1850, a protest resolution was drafted by male students at Harvard University to describe the position of men on women's acceptance of into medical school:

> *Resolved, that no woman of true delicacy would be willing in the presence of men to listen to the discussions of the subjects that necessarily come under the consideration of the student of medicine. Resolved, that we object to having the company of any female forced upon us, who is disposed to unsex herself, and to sacrifice her modesty by appearing with men in the lecture room.*[18]

Sadly, although Elizabeth Blackwell graduated from medical school as class valedictorian, not a single hospital or clinic in New York City would allow her to practice.

At the age of twenty-one, Susan was accepted at the Women's Medical College in Philadelphia, and she graduated three years later at the age of twenty-four. During school, Susan took courses in chemistry, anatomy, physiology, histology (cell and human tissues), pharmacy, diagnosis and management of specific diseases, obstetrics, dietetics, and women's health needs. She attended chemistry labs and anatomy labs. She dissected human cadavers, and memorized the name and location of every muscle, bone, and artery in the body.

As with many medical students before and after her, Susan liked the dissection lab and was amazed by the many small parts that were needed for the functioning of the human body.[19] She found chemistry tedious and difficult and was thrilled when she completed the course with an acceptable grade. At clinical practice sites, she learned how to write prescriptions, suture wounds, apply bandages, set bones, manage pain, and administer injections. She learned about infectious diseases such as tuberculosis, influenza, smallpox, measles, typhoid fever, dysentery, and cholera. She would have been introduced to the newly accepted "germ theory" and the importance of sanitation. She could perform basic surgeries and assist with childbearing. In 1889, there was little emphasis in medical schools on care of the mentally ill. Also, over 95 percent of the medicines and medical tools used by physicians today were not known when Susan attended school. After medical school, Susan was assigned internship for a year at the Woman's Hospital in Philadelphia.

Entering Medical Practice on the Macy Reservation. Following her internship, Susan obtained a government appointment and practiced as a doctor at the Macy reservation boarding school. Most of Susan's classmates set up their practices in the East, where medical facilities were better equipped than on the frontier, and salaries were certainly better. However, Susan wanted to serve her Omaha people.

As a physician at the reservation boarding school, Susan found the conditions at the school to be intolerable. She began to teach the importance of sanitation and personal hygiene. She emphasized to the administrators the importance of good ventilation and cleanliness. Because of Susan, vast improvements were made at the school. One example was the installation of a system of waterworks.

Following her practice at the boarding school, Susan was assigned as agency doctor over both the Winnebago and Macy (Omaha) reservations. As agency doctor, Susan provided medical care to 1,244 patients—Anglo Americans and Native Americans from both the Omaha and Winnebago tribes. She was immensely popular among people on the reservations and attracted new patients daily. She understood their language, was knowledgeable and skillful, caring, and concerned, and tribal members believed "she was one of them."

> *One time an eight-year-old boy became quite ill with a childhood ailment. Under Susan's care, he recovered rapidly from his condition. A day after treating that child, Susan rode on horseback eight miles*

into the country to see her young patient. She found him well and "splashing in a nearby creek—having an immense amount of fun." According to Susan, the boy's recovery won her "no end of fame.[20]

Even though life was challenging on the reservations, the Native Americans had made some progress in developing the land and their homes. The Omaha tribe now occupied 210 wood-frame houses.[21] They were becoming more involved with farming and livestock and were developing a reputation as good farmers. They wore white man's clothes and had farm equipment and machinery to work the land. In an 1890 report, the "Indian" agent "Robert Ashley" observed that *"the Omaha Indians have always been a quiet, peace-loving people, and easy to control."*[22]

Susan could only access patients in their homes on the reservation by travelling over rough dirt or icy roads. She made house calls in all kinds of weather. Initially, she visited patients by walking or horseback; later, she purchased a buggy for making visits. She frequently set out to visit patients at eight o'clock in the morning, and sometimes finished her rounds as late as 10:00 p.m. in the evening. When temperatures dropped to below freezing, Susan threw more buffalo robes around her shoulders and continued with her travels.

Susan was a physician who moved easily between the Anglo American and Native American cultures. She never refused to treat any patient who knocked on her door. She cared for patients even if they had no ability to pay her. When patients had no money for medicine, she used her own money. Too often, however, her reservation patients were extremely ill, and she had no hospital to send them to. Susan's work was praised by the Office of Indian Affairs (OIA). The only criticism of Susan was that she had "failed to transform the heathen women of the tribe into the paragon of Victorian womanhood." Susan responded that she was too busy providing medical care to deal with these matters. When Susan was first hired as an agency physician, her annual salary was $500. Two years later, she was given a pay raise, and her annual salary increased to $700 per year.

Combining Her Medical Career with Marriage and Children

One requirement for receiving funding for medical school was that Susan agreed not to marry until she had practiced as a doctor for at least two years. However, as with so many women before and after her, Susan wanted sometime in the future to have a marriage and children of her own.

In 1894 at the age of twenty-nine, Susan married thirty-four-year-old Henry Picotte, and she and Henry moved to Bancroft, Nebraska. Henry was the brother of the deceased Charles Picotte, who had been married to Susan's sister Marguerite. Henry Picotte was a handsome, semi-literate, mixed blood Yankton / Dakota Sioux. He was a former Wild West circus showman who drank alcohol on occasion. Susan's sisters and friends shared their misgivings about Henry with her. Susan was the only one of her sisters who did not marry an Anglo American. Her sisters believed that Henry was poorly educated, and far beneath Susan's station in life. *Henry was kind, considerate, and faithful,* however.[23]

After her marriage, Susan resigned as agency doctor at the OIA, and established a practice in her home in Bancroft as a private physician treating both Native and Anglo Americans. Susan's practice in Bancroft thrived, and she always had patients that needed her care. Susan and Henry had two sons, Caryl (born in 1895) and Pierre (born in 1898). Henry often cared for the children when Susan was seeing patients, and he even accompanied Susan on her buggy rides to patients when the weather was bad. When he could not care for them, the two boys rode with their mother on the back of her buggy. Caryl and Pierre both remembered spending a lot of time in their childhood riding in the back of a buggy.

During Susan's time living in Bancroft, she became friends with the renowned American writer and poet, John Neihardt. Neihardt was born in Sharpsburg, Illinois, in 1881. However, in 1901, he had moved to Bancroft, Nebraska, and became editor of the local newspaper, the *Bancroft Blade*. In Bancroft, he lived on the edge of the Macy reservation and a block away from Susan La Flesche, her husband Henry, and their two children. Neihardt spent many hours with the Omaha tribal people and elders and wrote extensively using Omaha tribal themes.

During his time with Susan, Neihardt was impressed by her dignity and professionalism. Upon meeting her, he recalled that "*she was tall, slender, black eyed, and bore herself with an air of dignified authority that made her seem far less gentle than she proved to be.*" He also believed that "*she was the most powerful public speaker he had ever heard.*"[24] Besides being honored as the first poet laureate for the state of Nebraska, Neihardt served as a professor of poetry at the University of Nebraska. Visitors can visit the John Neihardt study and garden at the Neihardt Center in Bancroft, Nebraska.

John Neihardt (1881-1973)
First poet laureate in state of Nebraska. Writer, poet, historian, ethnographer. Famous for writings on spirituality and Native Americans, Nebraska State Historical Society Photographic Collections.

Unfortunately, in 1905, Henry, who had been weakened by a lengthy battle with tuberculosis, died of alcohol abuse. When Henry died, he was forty-five and Susan was forty. With her husband's death, Susan moved back to Walthill and the Macy reservation. At her Walthill home, she entertained legislators, lawyers, and farmers, always advocating for justice for her Omaha people.[25] Susan was frail, and her health was often poor. She had severe ear, neck, and back pain, and later in life, she was diagnosed with cancer. Susan died in 1915 at the age of fifty.

Providing Medical Care to the Omaha Tribe in the 1890s

During her years in practice, Susan La Flesche managed a variety of medical problems for her people on the reservation.

She knew of her people's history and their struggles. In the 1890's, Omaha people had lived on the reservation for the last thirty to thirty-five years. They had learned not to trust the promises of the U.S. government or the agency doctors. Unlike previous doctors on the reservation, Susan knew her people's customs and language. She would have taken whatever time was needed to help her patients. She would have asked her patients respectful questions about their medical concerns and listened closely to their responses. She also knew that Omaha people considered every member of their tribe as a family member. Thus, she would have included family or other community members as needed in the plan of care.

Susan was aware that many of her patients suffered from malnutrition. When she was called to a patient's home, she knew that among other things, she would be encouraging rest, good nutrition, and extra fluids. She often carried extra food with her in her buggy and provided nutritious meals during her visits.

Susan saw patients with various aches and pains and skin rashes, and patients who were weary, depressed, and prematurely old. She cared for wounds and burns, sutured cuts, delivered babies, set broken bones, and managed patients with colds, stomach aches, life-threatening infectious diseases, and ailments of aging.

She treated burns by spreading ointment over the burned area as a protective barrier and to keep the wound from drying out. Next, the burn wound would be covered with a clean bandage. Susan closed open cuts in the skin using suture thread (silk or catgut) and needles to close the wound, and she would cover the wound with clean bandages.

One concern about wounds, even less severe ones, was that they could become infected. To prevent infections, Susan practiced good handwashing with soap and water before dressing wounds, and she always used clean instruments, suture threads, and bandages. She used copious quantities of clean water to flush out the wound and remove dirt and contaminants. She may have also cleansed the skin area around the wound with an antiseptic such as alcohol. When Susan visited patients, her black bag always contained suture needles, thread, clean bandages and needed medications.

Generally, Native Americans had fewer cavities in their teeth than Anglo Americans because they rarely ate sweets. Instead, they feasted on berries, vegetables, fry bread, and meat. In the 1890s, the treatment for people who had recurrent toothaches was to pull out the bothersome tooth, and dentists were rare on the Nebraska frontier. As with most physicians of her time, Susan kept tooth forceps in her medicine bag, and she pulled her patients' teeth when necessary. Many of the white settlers went to the local barber or blacksmith to have their teeth pulled, using either a forceps or pliers. When not carefully administered, pliers for pulling teeth can result in damage to the teeth and gums and even to fractured jaws. Pulling teeth in the 1890s could be a painful procedure.

Bone Setting on the reservation in the 1890's. Bones that were broken would require pulling and resetting, and bone setting could be extremely painful. Pain could be relieved by icing the limb and having the patient ingest an opium or whiskey or by giving an injection of morphine. Once the bone was reset, bandages were wrapped around the break. A splint or piece of wood and leather straps were used to keep the set bone in place. While broken bones may seem easy to fix in the modern world, they were not in the 1800s. Broken bones are extremely painful, and in the 1880s, bones would take a long time to heal. Also, they would not always heal in the correct position. In the 1890's, traction for broken bones and "Plaster of Paris" for casts was available. However, there is no documentation that they were used on reservations in the frontier west.

Managing Trachoma.[26] In the late 1800s, compared to Anglo Americans, Native Americans had more eye-related disorders. In the early 1910s, when statistics were first available, an estimated 33 percent of the Omaha people suffered from some form of eye contagion. The most serious eye disease Susan treated was "trachoma." Trachoma was an infection of the cornea (the anterior portion of the eyeball), and conjunctiva (the membrane covering the eyeball). The patient with trachoma complained of pain, sensitivity to light, and watering of the eye. Recovery from trachoma was slow, and some patients permanently lost their eyesight. Even today, trachoma is a major cause of blindness in many parts of the world. Trachoma is caused by *Chlamydia*, and treatments are antibiotics such as sulfonamide and tetracycline. Without antibiotics, Susan's only treatment was the use of eye washes. Susan would also emphasize prevention of eye disease. She instructed all tribal people to practice good hand washing, to use clean, non-contaminated water, to not touch their eyes with their hands, and to not touch articles used by others with the infection. Patients with the infection were instructed to use separate towels and basins.

Assisting with Childbirth.[27] In the 1800's, about one of every 100 births led to the mother's death. Deaths during childbirth occurred even more frequently when women were ill or malnourished. Also, since women gave birth much more often than today, maternal deaths were not uncommon. Thus, even in the 1800s, most women survived childbirth and had healthy babies. When there were complications, however, childbirth could be deadly. There is little documentation about problems with childbirth prior to the twentieth century. In the past, it seems historians believed childbirth was a delicate subject, not something appropriate to write about.

Generally, Native American women had an easier time with childbirth than Anglo American women. Native women generally weighed less, and their babies were smaller. Compared to Anglo American women, their time of labor was shorter, seldom more than four hours, and the delivery was slightly less painful. Tribal midwives assisted women in childbirth. Pregnant women and babies were honored by their tribe. During childbirth, most women were provided special tipis or lodges. Prayers and chants were conducted outside of the tent to ensure that the labor and delivery went well. Often, Native American women went back to work a few days after childbirth. In contrast, Anglo women at that time, especially if they were upper-class women, spent weeks on bedrest following delivery of a child.

Women generally died during childbirth because of infections (often due to poor sanitation procedures), bleeding, and prolonged labor. Prolonged labor could be due to a smaller birth canal or the baby presenting in the wrong position for delivery. If the baby's head was not progressing through a smaller birth canal, doctors would attach forceps to the head and attempt to pull the baby through the canal. When the baby was in the wrong position, it was called a breech birth. The baby needed to be turned Internally so that it could be delivered head-first.

Historically, both Native and Anglo-American women who were giving birth were attended by other women—family members, friends, or midwives. Men were often not allowed to be present with women at the time of labor and delivery. When complications occurred, the assistance of doctors and instruments such as forceps were required. Before knowledge of the importance of sanitation, doctor's hands and instruments could be contaminated. Women in labor would have been better off without the assistance of these doctors. In addition, male doctors were often uncomfortable treating female patients. In accordance with the culture of the time, men were not expected to observe bodies of women who were not their wives.

Susan was generally more successful in helping with childbirth than the male doctors in her area. She knew the importance of sanitation procedures. She had learned how to turn babies in the breech position during her time with tribal midwives, and, compared to her male peers, she was more comfortable treating female patients. An anecdote from one of the readings described a time when two Anglo American male doctors in the area were having difficulty managing a childbirth, and the mother was exhausted. The two doctors were concerned that they might lose both the mother and the baby, because the labor and delivery were taking too long. They asked for Susan's help, and with her assistance, both the mother and baby survived.

Today, forceps are generally not used for prolonged labor. Instead, more women are having surgery (Caesarian sections) when labor is prolonged, and this surgery would require hospitalization. Women with infections and bleeding can be treated with intravenous antibiotics and blood transfusions. Unfortunately, there are still incidents today of women dying in childbirth, especially when they have insufficient access to medical care.

Opening the Walthill Hospital in 1913

During her practice, Susan saw the need for a hospital on the Macy Reservation for women having complications with childbirth, for the seriously ill, and to isolate patients with infectious diseases. In 1913, the Walthill hospital was opened, largely because of her efforts. The land was donated for the hospital site, and Susan raised the money for building the hospital from private donations. She helped with the design of the hospital. There were examining tables, surgical suites, hospital wards, and a morgue. Susan insisted on a screened-in porch that was the entire length of the hospital. Patients could be moved to the porch so that they could experience the fresh air and sunshine. Susan considered the building of the hospital one of her greatest achievements.[28]

FOUR

Diagnostic Tools and Medicines in the 1890s

In the 1890s, medical treatment was often primitive, and diseases that are considered curable today were often fatal. Unfortunately, on the reservation, the government often neglected to provide even basic drugs and medical supplies. Or medications that were needed would be late in arriving. In addition, Susan also had difficulty convincing some of her Omaha patients to accept her prescribed medications. She often supplemented these medications with the herbs and wild plants she had learned about as a child when observing traditional tribal healers. It was not unusual to see Susan La Flesche, with her learned doctoral degree, digging out plants and roots in the grasslands to be used in herbal therapies, because she had no other recourse.

Susan believed in the Native American philosophy of health. In addition to herbal medications, she incorporated other aspects of Indian healing, such as use of prayers and sweat lodges. She relied on her Christian beliefs when dealing with the tremendous challenges to medical care in the late 1800s. She believed that the Great Spirit had several names. The Omaha Indians called the Great Spirit "Wakonda," and the Christians worshiped a Great Spirit named "Jesus Christ." Susan was not only a doctor. She was also a nurse, teacher, social worker, counselor, leader, and advocate for justice for her tribe.

Chapter four describes the diagnostic tests, vaccinations, and medications available to Dr. Susan La Flesche in the 1890s.

Diagnostic Tools in the 1890s

Due to the paucity of diagnostic tests, Susan depended on her clinical visits and assessment to diagnose and care for her patients. Just like doctors before and after Susan, when she visited patients, she carried her diagnostic tools and medications in a sturdy black bag. Initially, she interviewed her patients about their illness and about illnesses currently experienced by other Omaha people on the reservation. She asked her patients about the problems they were having that she could help with. Were they having pain, a cough, or an upset stomach? She examined their mouth and throat, their skin color, and their breathing pattern.[1] Were there any skin rashes or skin breaks? If bleeding was present, she estimated how much blood the patient was losing. If the patient had pain, she estimated how badly the patient was hurting, and where the pain came from. She took the patient's temperature and pulse, and she listened to their heart, lungs, and abdomen with her stethoscope. Even smells were important. The patient's breath and urine were important for detecting everything from tuberculosis to diabetes. Patients with tuberculosis had breath that reflected the decay in their lungs. Patients with diabetes had sugar in their urine, and their urine tasted sweet.

Both stethoscopes and clinical thermometers were available for patient examination and diagnosis in the 1890s. Stethoscopes were originally invented as early as 1816 by the French physician Rene Laennec. However, the early stethoscopes were not extremely useful or accurate. It was not until the 1880s that stethoscopes were introduced with flexible rubber tubes that could fit in both ears. With stethoscopes, physicians could hear heart, lung, and bowel sounds, and they could more easily detect heart problems, pneumonias, and bowel problems.

Glass thermometers were invented in the late 1860s, and with these portable thermometers, fevers could be diagnosed in less than five minutes. Unfortunately, because they were glass, they could break easily. Susan reported that when she rode on horseback to visit a patient, by the time she arrived at the visit many of the thermometers she had packed were broken.[2]

For most of her practice, Susan would not have been able to take blood pressure measurements on her home visits to patients. The first sphygmomanometer was not developed by an Austrian physician, Karl Samuel Ritter, until 1881. The first cuff-based mercury sphygmomanometer that allowed blood pressures to be measured in clinics was not developed until 1896. There was not widespread use of cuff-based sphygmomanometers until 1920. Although opthalmoscopes or scopes of the eyes had been invented, most likely Susan did not have them on patient visits. Patients who complained that their eyes were not allowing them to read letters clearly were asked to try on numerous eyeglasses of different strengths. They chose among the available glasses the ones that were most helpful for their sight

In her later years of her practice, X-rays were being used to assist in diagnosis of an illness.[3] William Roentgen introduced x-rays to the medical world in 1895. X-rays changed medical diagnostics and medical treatment for the better. With x-rays, doctors could clearly observe problems, such as broken bones, fluid in the lungs (pneumonia), and bowel obstructions. Unfortunately, early x-ray workers had no knowledge of the dangers of the radiation this tool emits, and they developed ulcers, lesions, and even cancers from their exposure to x-rays.

With the discovery of the burning power of x-rays, researchers realized that radiation could also be used to destroy cancerous tumors. In the early 1900s, Marie Curie of France used radium, a therapeutic form of radiation, to treat cancer patients. She received the Nobel prize for her work with radium and cancer. In 1915, at the age of fifty, Susan suffered a painful death from what was believed to be facial bone cancer. Her family had arranged to have radium shipped from Marie Curie's laboratory in Paris hoping that the radium could control the cancer. Hopefully with radium, Susan's life could be prolonged. The radium arrived in Nebraska too late for Susan. She was already dying.

Diagnostic Tools Today[4]

Since the early 1900s, new tools have been developed that have improved the accuracy of diagnosis. Today, there are accurate otoscopes and ophthalmoscopes for examining ears and eyes and diagnosing infections. In addition to x-rays, we now have ultrasounds that use high frequency sound waves to examine internal organs. Computer axial tomography (CAT) scanning combines x-rays with computer analyses to create three dimensional views of internal organs, and these scans are especially useful for examining bone, skull, and head injuries. With Magnetic Resonance Imagining (MRI), powerful magnetic fields can create three-dimensional images of soft tissues. Fiber-optic endoscopes can be inserted into body openings and allow a direct view of the inside of the gastrointestinal tract.

Blood tests can detect abnormalities in the blood or in organ functioning. Because of the human genome project, patients can have medications especially made for them that are specific for their genetic (RNA and DNA) makeup. The diagnostic tools prescribed in the above paragraph are but a few of the many tools available to physicians today. Susan La Flesche would agree, however, that one should never underestimate the importance of the doctor's examination and interview of the patient in diagnosing the patient's medical needs.[5]

Vaccinations in the 1890s and Today

Except for the smallpox vaccine, no vaccines were available to prevent diseases in the 1890s. Vaccinations were especially critical for prevention of viral diseases such as smallpox, influenza, and measles. While antibiotics work with many bacterial infections (*e.g.*, dysentery, cholera, typhoid, and tuberculosis), historically viral infections have been extremely difficult to treat and to cure. When a patient is vaccinated, a small amount of the virus causing the infection is injected into the patient. The amount of virus injected would not be enough to cause an illness. However, this small amount of virus would be enough to produce "host" immunity, whereby the patient can resist or overcome exposure to the infection. The development and use of vaccinations have saved millions of lives.

Edward Jenner[6] is credited with developing the first effective vaccine. In 1796, he developed a vaccine for protection against smallpox. He had noticed that during a smallpox outbreak, milkmaids rarely caught the disease. They did, however, become infected with a disease called cowpox, and this was the result of touching the udders of infected cows. Cowpox did cause unsightly pustules (skin elevations containing pus), but this disease was not fatal. Jenner discovered that by scratching the skin of patients and injecting the pus from cowpox, the patient became immune to smallpox. The word "vaccine" was derived from the Latin term for cows, "vacca." Smallpox vaccinations became widely available to Anglo Americans in 1818, but not to Native Americans.

In 1832, the U.S. government did initiate a program to vaccinate Native Americans. However, not all of them received the vaccine, Also, the quality of the smallpox vaccine for all Americans was a concern as late as 1866. In 1866, at the end of the Civil War, there was an outbreak of smallpox in African American soldiers. The military believed the outbreak was due to "bad" vaccine. As a result, these soldiers received new vaccinations.

A vaccine for cholera was developed in 1879; typhoid fever in 1896; tuberculosis in 1927; influenza in 1945; and measles in 1963.[7] There was generally a delay between the times vaccinations were developed and the time they were administered to large numbers of people.

Medications in the 1890s

Writers have referred to the time around the Civil War as the "Middle Ages "of medicine. Most medications used in the 1800s were primitive by today's standards, and few could cure a disease.[8]

In the 1800s, the role of doctors and pharmacists in prescribing, mixing, and dispensing medications were overlapping. Most medications were either in liquid or powder form, and doctors mixed and dispensed their own medications. Susan La Flesche had a "hi-speed dispenser" that she used both to mix medications and to dispense the correct amount or dosage. She learned about available medications to prescribe in medical school. In addition to prescribed medications, she commonly used the herbal treatments she had learned from her Omaha tribe. Some of the medications most likely used by Susan La Flesche in the 1890s are listed in the following paragraphs.[9]

For patients complaining of *constipation*, Susan could have dispensed castor oil or Epsom salts. Castor oil had been used to treat constipation since the 1700s, and was a favorite medication of President George Washington's wife, Martha. Epsom salts (magnesium sulfate) are also used as a mild laxative. There were harsher cathartics or laxatives. One medication patented by Dr. Benjamin Rush called "Rush's" pills was a combination of Calomel and Jalap and truly caused "explosive diarrhea" that "purged" the bowels. Opiate products such as Paregoric and Laudanum were used to treat patients complaining of *diarrhea*. Paregoric was an elixir consisting of a tincture of opium with camphor. Laudanum was an elixir consisting of opium and an alcohol such as wine.

Susan could prescribe Phenacetin for *mild pain and fever*. Phenacetin was not an opium derivative and was the first synthetic pain medication. If willow trees were available, the leaves and bark of the willow tree were used to reduce mild pain and fever. Willow bark contained salicin which converts to salicylic acid. Salicin was later used as the main component of Aspirin. One concern was that too much salicin caused stomach cramping. Aspirin (acetylsalicylic acid) was discovered in 1853 and was more widely prescribed than "salicin" because there was not the stomach cramping. Although Aspirin was produced in quantities in 1875, it was not until the 1900s that physicians prescribed it routinely for their patients. At least early in her practice, Susan most likely did not have access to Aspirin. She also treated fevers with cold packs and by recommending to patients that they drink more fluids.

Susan may have prescribed cocaine to relieve the *pain of toothaches* or to reduce pain when pulling teeth. Cocaine could also be prescribed to relieve headaches and for hay fever and cough because the drug did reduce swelling or inflammation. Cocaine (cocaine hydrochloride) was isolated from coco leaves and was first used in the U.S. in 1859. It was available in powder form and was used as a local anesthetic to dull pain in the skin. Cocaine has little effect on unbroken skin, but is rapidly absorbed through the mucous membranes, such as the inside of the mouth, nose, or the inside of wounds.

In the 1800s, cocaine was widely available in drug stores and was added to multiple different medications. Unfortunately, use of cocaine has the potential to be abused. Cocaine is not physically addictive, but use of cocaine can result in psychological dependence. A moderate dose of the drug creates the feeling of stimulation, well-being, and overconfidence. Cocaine overdose can lead to dizziness, fainting, and convulsions.

In the U.S. today, cocaine is commonly used in the form of an illegal drug labelled "crack." Both cocaine and crack have the same ingredients and are essentially the same drug. Powdered cocaine can be snorted, swallowed, and injected, while crack is smoked. The result is that crack has a quicker onset of action than powdered cocaine and can last longer. Crack is sold illegally and widely abused today. The medical and behavioral problems in the U.S. today resulting from crack have reached epidemic proportions.

Laudanum and morphine were derivatives of opium and commonly used for *moderate and severe pain* in the 1800s. Heroin, the "heroic" drug derived from morphine, was also used, not so much for pain, but more often for asthma and cough. Laudanum was administered as a syrup, and morphine was best absorbed when used as an injection. Laudanum was used for pain management, headaches, anxiety, insomnia, diarrhea, toothaches, and was even provided to quiet fussy babies. Scientists had discovered that opiates were more easily dissolved in alcohol than in water. Thus, the best strategy for making an elixir or liquid opium was to dissolve the opium in an alcohol such as wine or whiskey. Laudanum was an opium made into an elixir by mixing it with wine, often flavored with Cinnamon or saffron.

Morphine was named after "Morpheus," the "God of Sleep." It was not well absorbed when taken by mouth or orally. Thus, after development of the hypodermic syringe in 1853, morphine was administered by injection and was used by surgeons in the Civil war to provide quick relief to injured Confederate and Union soldiers. Morphine could also be used as a powder that was spread directly on the soldier's wounds. In the 1800s, when used appropriately, medications that contained opium such as Laudanum and morphine were useful for patients. However, these medications could also be misused and harmful.

Chloroform and ether were available to anesthetize the patient when performing surgeries. Nitrous oxide was also available as an *anesthetic*, and because it was short-acting, nitrous oxide was more likely to be used for minor surgeries such as extraction of decayed teeth. Chloral Hydrate was synthesized by Justin Liebig in 1831, and in 1869 was used to *promote drowsiness and sleep*. This drug was still used in practice until 2012 when safer medications for sleep were developed.

Some antiseptics had been developed to cleanse living tissue of pathological organisms. Disinfectants were also developed to cleanse inanimate objects such as counter tops of pathological organisms. Camphor prevented infections that could result from breaks in the skin. Camphor was also used to provide relief for minor skin burns, skin itches, and insect stings. This topical medication was derived from the wood and bark of camphor trees. Carbolic acid, bromine, and phenol were *antiseptics* that could prevent infections during performance of surgeries. In the 1800s, physicians used whiskey as a painkiller, sedative, antiseptic, and disinfectant. On the television show, *Gunsmoke,* Doc Adams always carried whiskey in his black bag. Susan abhorred the use of whiskey, at least for recreational purposes. Whiskey is no longer considered a medication. However, a component of whiskey, ethyl alcohol, continues to be used as a topical antiseptic and disinfectant.

Miscellaneous Drugs. In the 1880s, baking soda was useful to *relieve the itch* from skin rashes. The plant "Aloe Vera" could be applied for the relief of dry skin. Boric acid solutions were available for *relief of dry eyes.* Ergot was used first by midwives, then later by physicians to *stimulate childbirth* in women when labor was slow, and to reduce bleeding after childbirth. Quinine was available for *treatment of malaria.* Quinine had also been commonly used to reduce pain and fever. Quinine is an effective drug for treating malaria and is still used infrequently for pain management in patients with certain types of arthritis (inflammation and destruction of joints), such as psoriatic and rheumatoid arthritis. However, quinine would most likely not be effective in managing other types of pain. Quinine was developed from the bark of the Cinchona (quinaquina) tree.

Patients in the 1800s also suffered from "dropsy" or swelling of the lower legs. Dropsy was due to a heart condition, and the drug digitalis was available in the 1800s to *stimulate the heart.* Digitalis improved blood circulation and consequently worked as a diuretic to stimulate urination and reduce swelling. Digitalis was extracted from the foxglove plant (*Digitalis purpurae).* Currently, digitalis is still prescribed for heart conditions, but infrequently, because newer drugs have been found to be more effective and less toxic. Colchicine, derived from the seeds and root of the plant *Colchicum autumnale* (meadow saffron) has been used for hundreds of years, and is still used today for the *treatment of gout.* Gout is a disease that causes pain and tenderness in the joints due to increased uric acid in the blood and deposits of uric acid in the joints.

Medication Quackery. In the 1800s, given the population's lack of trust in a doctor's ability to cure disease, unscrupulous manufacturers[10] used clever marketing to sell medications that were ineffective and sometimes even dangerous. These medications were often "patented" into pills, tonics, and potions, and were given fancy names such as "Parker's Ginger Tonic" and "Simmons Liver Regulator." Even Wyatt Earp and Doc Holliday carried Simmons Liver Regulator with them to save them from "bilious" attacks, such as nausea and vomiting. In fact, Simmons Liver Regulator was useless. Charlatans or "snake oil" salespeople would travel from town to town pedaling their useless wares. The name "snake oil" came about because oil from snakes was believed to be a particularly valuable remedy, especially oil from rattle snakes. One product that sold well was scorpion oil as a treatment for venereal disease. These "quack" medications were even advertised in popular magazines such as *Harper's Magazine, Collier's*, and *Atlantic Monthly.*

In the 1800s, there were no medications that could be prescribed to effectively treat depression or "melancholy." Abraham Lincoln had been treated for "melancholy" with "blue mass" (*Pitula hydrargyri*) or Calomel. Calomel was mentioned earlier because it was also a harsh laxative used in "Rush's" pills. This medication was not helpful for treating depression; Calomel contained mercury, which caused neurological changes in patients and was toxic. It seems as if certain doctors in the 1800s were told by their professors "when in doubt, give Calomel." Prior to his Inauguration, President Lincoln had intense mood swings and often raged in anger. He stopped taking "blue mass" or Calomel soon after his inauguration, and during his term as president, he was known as a very calm and reflective president. During her years of practice, Susan La Flesche's most common prescriptions for depression were exercise and fresh air, "*Plenty of air and sunshine—that is Nature's Medicine, but I have hard work to make people understand.*[11]

Dr. Benjamin Rush was a distinguished physician at the end of the 1700s who patented a pill called "Rush's" pills, and he recommended that these pills be used for all ailments. He believed that all diseases originated in the bowels, and the best way to treat or even cure disease was to empty the bowels. Because of his recommendation, Lewis and Clark carried hundreds of "Rush's" pills on their expedition west. The result was that by the time the expedition reached Oregon, many of the men in the expedition were weak from diarrhea.

Opium Addiction. Opium derivatives that were a major cause of drug addiction in the 1800s were Laudanum and morphine. Opium was derived from poppy seeds and has been used since the time of Socrates. The recreational use of smoking opium was introduced to the U.S. by Chinese workers in the 1840s and 1850s. Chinese workers had come to the U.S. to work in the California gold mines and later to work on the transcontinental railroad.

The opium derivative "Laudanum" was an elixir that was cheap (less expensive than alcohol) and easily accessible in the 1800s. Unquestionably, Laudanum provided relief to multiple patients. However, the drug could also cause addiction and the numerous problems associated with it. Too often, this liquid medication was used indiscriminately, even though the medication bottle was clearly marked as poison.

In the 1800s, opium was not a restricted drug. Men and women kept a medication bottle of Laudanum in their medicine cabinets in the same way patients today keep Tylenol in their cabinets. Medical use often turned into habitual use, and many people began to take the drug recreationally.

One long-standing belief has been that use and addiction to Laudanum and other opium products were most common in people from the lower classes—men and women of ill repute who were perhaps alcoholics or prostitutes. Documentation from the time, however, shows that habitual use was common in patients from all socioeconomic classes. Studies have found that, in the 1800s, more women than men were users of Laudanum, and fewer than one-third of these women were prostitutes.

Laudanum
Liquid derivative of opium. Illustration by Erica Parker Rogers.

The most common method of committing suicide for women in the 1800s was the ingestion of copious amounts of Laudanum. When women in upper and middle classes committed suicide, the cause of death was not released to the public. Suicide was kept a family secret. However, suicides in women of lower classes and in prostitutes were publicly reported. Prostitutes in Cheyenne, Wyoming, in 1883; in Virginia City, Nevada, in 1875; and Bodie, California, in 1879 were all reported as committing suicide by using Laudanum.

Addiction to opium derivatives became an even more serious social crisis during and after the Civil War. Over 100,000 soldiers who received morphine injections or pills during the war continued to use morphine and other opiate derivatives after the war. Because of the number of veteran's addicted, opium dependence became known as the "old soldier's disease."

In 2017, Miroff wrote an article in the *Washington Post* about the drug problem in the U.S., beginning in the 1800s: "*Americans have become the greatest drug fiends in the world. Anguished veterans were hooked on morphine. Genteel 'society ladies' dosed up with Laudanum—a tincture of alcohol and opium. The wonder drug was widely used to suppress cough and treat diarrhea in children."*[12]

In 1909, the problem of addiction was addressed by an international commission, and the first steps were taken to control and regulate opium. In 1914, President Woodrow Wilson signed the Harrison Act banning the nonmedical use of opium and morphine Finally, in 1942, the U.S. Congress passed the Opium Control Act making it unlawful for any person to produce the opium poppy, except under license. Licenses were only issued if necessary to supply the medical and scientific needs of the U.S.

Today, opiate drugs are restricted, and their prescriptions and use are carefully monitored. Trafficking illegal opiate drugs can result in extended prison sentences. Numerous programs have been developed to treat drug addictions. Unfortunately, opiate abuse remains a widespread and critical problem worldwide and in the U.S. for all Americans, including Native Americans. This epidemic has resulted in death and destruction, with no end in sight.

Medications Today [13]

The first antibiotic developed for treatment of infectious diseases was sulfa (sulfanilamide) in 1935. Sulfa drugs were effective against bacterial infections and were lifesaving. An even better antibiotic for treating bacterial infections was penicillin. Penicillin *(penicillium notatum)* was truly a wonder drug, discovered by Alexander Fleming in 1929, and used in the 1940s to treat numerous types of bacterial diseases. Penicillin is believed to have saved the lives of thousands of service members wounded in battle in World War II. Streptomycin, the first antibiotic effective against tuberculosis, was developed in 1944. Insulin was discovered in the 1920s for treatment of diabetes. Prior to insulin, diabetes was considered a fatal disease.

Anti-depressive and anti-psychotic medications have improved the lives of patients with mental health problems. We now have powerful new drugs to treat cancer, pulmonary and heart diseases, HIV, and AIDs. Oral contraceptives perfected in the 1950s now allow women to plan the size of their families. Heart, liver, lung, and kidney transplants are possible. Kidney dialysis machines can keep patients with failing kidneys alive until transplants are possible. Scientists are always searching for ways to extend our survival time and to improve our quality of life. Because of modern medicine, people are living longer than ever before. The quality of our lives today is much better than the quality of lives of people in the late 1800s.[14]

Susan La Flesche started her practice soon after there was general acceptance in the U.S. that infectious diseases were caused by germs. This acceptance of the "germ theory" greatly impacted Susan's priorities in providing care to her patients. She understood that her most important role was not prescriptions for medications. Her priority was to teach her patients the importance of healthy living and prevention of illnesses—especially prevention of infectious diseases. She believed that prevention meant sanitation, and the Omaha people had little understanding of the importance of sanitation in preventing the spread of disease.

FIVE

The Germ Theory

Chapter five describes the devastation of infectious diseases in Native Americans throughout history, the acceptance of germs as causing infections in the 1880s, the importance of sanitation and public health measures in preventing infections, and Susan La Flesche's fight to improve hygiene and sanitation measures on the reservation.

The Tragic Consequences of the Columbian Exchange

Numerous epidemics of infectious diseases have occurred in America since the 1400s, and Native Americans have suffered more from these diseases than any other race or ethnicity.

The "Columbian Exchange" is the label used today to describe the cross-continental transfer of plants, animals, cultures, and diseases that occurred in the late 1400s and 1500s. Christopher Columbus and his crew arrived in the Caribbean in 1492. Columbus believed he had arrived in the "Indies," and as a result, indigenous people were renamed "Indians." Unfortunately, the infectious diseases Columbus brought ravaged the indigenous people who had no previous exposure to these diseases and no "host immunity," or ability to resist or overcome exposure to them.

Infectious diseases introduced by Europeans in the 1400s and 1500s causing the greatest number of deaths were measles, smallpox, typhoid fever, cholera, malaria, and influenza. Smallpox was "captain of the men of death" and measles was the "first lieutenant." There were also many other diseases introduced by the Europeans including typhus, mumps, whooping cough, and yellow fever. Native Americans are believed to have suffered from tuberculosis, dysentery, and pneumonia even prior to the Columbian Exchange. These diseases became even more prevalent and deadly as more Anglo Americans settled in the "New World." The social changes that resulted from contact with European outsiders almost certainly created the conditions that converted endemic (localized) tuberculosis into epidemic (widespread) tuberculosis.

The indigenous population of North and South America prior to Columbus decreased by 60 percent because of diseases introduced by the Europeans. Originally, there were between 40 and 100 million indigenous people in the Americas. From the years 1492 to 1650, epidemics of infectious diseases (mostly smallpox and measles) decreased that number to twenty-four million or less. According to Osterholm and Olshaker, *"Infectious disease is the deadliest enemy faced by all humankind."*[1]

Due to the impact of epidemic diseases, countless lives have been lost, civilizations destroyed, nations disrupted, armies defeated, and economic development halted.[2] Villages have been abandoned or consolidated, social, and political structures have been broken, and knowledge has been lost.

> *The entire history of the Americas might have played out differently if the disease transmission pattern had gone the other way—if European soldiers and settlers had been repeatedly wiped out by epidemics at the same 60 to 90 percent mortality rate of smallpox as the Indigenous people. It's possible the Europeans would have even given up entirely on their early attempts at settlement. Maybe the history of the 'New World' would have played out very differently as a result.*[3]

Infectious Diseases and the Omaha Tribe

During the 1700s and 1800s, most of the Omaha people did not die from warfare or accidents or old age. Rather, they died from infectious diseases that today could have been preventable. Five of the diseases most common and deadly for the Omaha tribe were tuberculosis, influenza, smallpox, measles, and dysentery. Typhoid fever and cholera also occurred in the Nebraska Territory, but incidences were fewer in number. The diseases listed above will be the focus of chapters six, seven, and eight.

Epidemiological Transition: Decrease in Death Rate from Infectious Diseases

From 1890 to 1930, there was a shift in leading causes of death for all Americans, including Native Americans. The shift was from infectious diseases as leading causes of death to degenerative diseases such as heart disease, cancer, and strokes. This decrease in deaths from infectious diseases was largely due to the development of vaccines and antibiotics and was also the result of general acceptance of the "germ theory." Physicians and other health care providers in the U.S. were beginning to understand that germs caused diseases and that practicing sanitation procedures prevented the spread of these deadly germs. Even in the 1800s, patients could die of cancer and heart disease. "*However, before 1930, infectious diseases got to people earlier and more often than heart disease or cancer ever could.*"[4]

Prior to the knowledge of the "Germ Theory," lack of sanitation had deadly results.

Lack of Sanitation during the Civil War. Up until the twentieth century, more people died on the battlefield from infectious diseases than from war wounds. During the Civil War from 1860 to 1865, and between the north and south, over 600,000 soldiers died, and two-thirds of these soldiers died from infectious diseases. Epidemics from infectious diseases played a key role in halting major campaigns and are believed to have prolonged fighting for as long as two years.

The Civil War was the last large-scale conflict fought without practitioners' knowledge that germs caused disease. Comprehensive health records are available from the Civil War supporting poor sanitation as a cause of these deadly infectious diseases. Fatal diseases resulting in death were primarily pneumonia, typhoid, malaria, measles, tuberculosis, smallpox, and dysentery. Reasons for the proliferation of infectious diseases during the war are described in the following paragraph.

Soldiers were not practicing personal hygiene and bathing was infrequent. "*Because soldiers rarely had the opportunity to bathe, it was said a Civil War army on the march could be smelled before it could be seen.*"[5] Food was spoiled, and dietary deficiencies led to malnutrition. Soldiers slept in overcrowded tents, and this resulted in the spread of fatal bouts of both influenza and measles. Cold rains and walking in mud were frequent, water was contaminated, and clothing was inadequate for weather conditions. Malaria, typhoid, and cholera were contracted from the water and from wading in the Mississippi swamps. Battle wounds were not properly cleansed, and campfire smoke caused the soldiers to develop bronchitis. At the time of the Civil War, doctors could unknowingly infect their own patients by spreading germs from one person to another. They often did not change clothes, clean their instruments, or even wash their hands after treating one patient and moving on to another.

The smallpox vaccine had been available in America since 1818. However, smallpox did occur among the soldiers, especially among the African American soldiers who had not been vaccinated or had received vaccines of poor quality. Although not always deadly, the most common infectious disease among soldiers was dysentery. The largest number of deaths from infectious diseases occurred in the Union (northern) and Confederate (southern) prisons, where conditions were truly deplorable.

Although Nebraska did not become a state until 1867, Omaha tribal members did enlist and contribute to the Union war effort. Numerous Native Americans enlisted as soldiers in the Civil War, both in Union and Confederate armies. Several of them obtained the rank of Brigadier General during their service in the war. However, most Native Americans at that time were being forced to live on reservations.

Lack of Sanitation and the Omaha tribe in the 1800s. The causes and impact of infectious diseases in Omaha people were like the causes and impact of diseases in Civil War soldiers. Forced moves to reservations were major contributors to the increased incidence of infectious diseases.

Omaha people were displaced from rural settings and forcibly moved to reservations where they experienced overcrowding, lack of opportunities for personal hygiene, and contaminated water supplies. They had little access to health care and had little understanding of the importance of sanitation in preventing disease. They suffered malnutrition and became ill from lack of food or eating spoiled food. They were forced to migrate to new areas where they had increased contact with new insects and animals. Finally, moves to reservations and more exposure to Anglo Americans resulted in Omaha people being exposed to infections they had no immunity against.

Unfortunately, during the Civil War, the U.S government paid little attention to the plight of the Native Americans who were not at war but were forced to move to reservations. Once the war had ended, President Grant did express concern about the corrupt agents who were assigned to supervise reservations. He instituted a peace policy to remove the present agents and replace them with Christian missionaries. However, the missionaries took more freedoms away from the Native Americans than had the previous agents. There was no effort to improve access to food supplies or sanitation procedures.

Prior to the late 1800s, no one knew how best to prevent and treat infectious diseases.

Imbalance in the Four Humors

Historically, causes of disease were unknown. The Greek physicians in 450 BC proposed that illness was related to an imbalance of the four humors—blood, phlegm (pus), yellow bile, and black bile. There was no understanding of separate, distinct diseases. There was just one malady that caused all diseases and that was an imbalance in humors.[6]

This theory of humors was later supported by one of the most eminent physicians and leading medical thinkers in the 1700s, Dr. Benjamin Rush. Dr. Rush is often considered the "Father of American Medicine." He lived in Philadelphia, Pennsylvania, and was one of the original signers of the

Declaration of Independence. Therapies prescribed by Dr. Rush to treat illnesses and to balance the humors included bleeding or bloodletting, purging (either by emetics causing vomiting or harsh laxatives or enemas), and blistering. Dr. Rush also believed that bad air or "miasma" was a cause of illness. Miasma will be addressed later in this chapter.

Bloodletting, Purging, and Blistering.[7]

Bloodletting was practiced because of the belief that patients with an illness had an excess of blood due to inflammation (damaged tissue).[8] This practice involved removing large quantities of blood from patients by cutting a vein and allowing the blood to drain out. "*The sicker the patient, the more blood was drained.*"[9] Dr. Rush believed that, in extreme cases, two-thirds of the blood in the body should be removed· Since the body typically contains six quarts of blood, this would require removal of over four quarts of blood. Our first U.S. president, George Washington, was an unfortunate victim of bloodletting. He went to his physicians for treatment of a sore throat and was bled repeatedly with the hope of curing his illness. By the end of the day, George Washington was dead. The practice of bloodletting most certainly hastened his death.

Before the 1880s, mental illness was not well understood, and treatment was rare or non-existent. Mentally ill people were considered evil or immoral and were often chained in asylums or county jails.[10] Dr. Rush believed that mental illness was a result of too much blood in the brain, and advocated for his favorite treatment, bloodletting. Removing copious quantities of blood did appear to have a calming (or exhausting effect), and this practice for treating mental illness was continued through most of the nineteenth century. Obviously though, bloodletting did not effectively cure mental illness or any other disease.

From 1850 to 1900, medical professionals also appeared to be obsessed with treating illness by cleansing out the bowels. Along with bloodletting, Dr. Rush believed that an imbalance in humors could also be addressed by "purging the gut."[11] This could be accomplished by the patient ingesting strong cathartics such as Calomel and Jalap or by using enemas to cleanse the bowels. Cathartics were commonly called "physics," and enemas were called "clysters."

A popular cathartic pill patented by Rush was a mixture of Calomel and Jalap, called "Rush's" pills or "thunder clappers."[12] These pills resulted in a violent purging of the bowels.

One less common therapy for balancing the humor of phlegm (or pus) was "blistering."[13] Blistering was especially used for stomach ailments because internal surgery was unknown. This was the practice of placing irritating chemical agents on a selected portion of the patient's skin to induce a burn. Even steaming hot poultices could scald the skin and create burns that later became infected. It was believed that the resulting pus flowing from the burn wound was beneficial.

After reading about bleeding, purging, and blistering, one would agree with Francis Bacon's comment about "Early American Medicine." After studying medicine practiced in the 1700s and 1800s, he wrote that "*one can only conclude that the remedy is worse than the disease.*"[14]

Long before Dr. Benjamin Rush, another physician who attempted to understand illness and healing and to document his belief in his writings was Hippocrates (460–370 BC). Hippocrates is often called the "Father of Medicine." He wrote over fifty books, and his beliefs about healing are still used in medical schools today. He believed that diseases were not caused by gods or demons.[15] Instead, they were due to either the condition of the human body or by environmental conditions. Unfortunately, partially based on his works, his followers proposed that diseases were caused by either an "imbalance in humors" or by bad air, "miasma."[16]

The Theory that Miasma Caused Infectious Disease

"Miasma" came from the Greek word for pollution and was also referred to as "bad air." The concept of miasma was pervasive among physicians in the U.S. and in Europe from the time of Hippocrates all the way to the nineteenth century.[17] This bad air supposedly originated from putrid waste (miasmatics) that would rise from sewage disposal and smelly swamps. Miasmata would ruin water, air, and nearby food, cause widespread sickness and could be identified by the unpleasant odor of rot.

In the U.S., even before discovery of the germ theory, belief in miasma did lead to real gains in sanitation.[18] Boards of health began to emphasize the importance of handwashing, cleanliness, and proper disposal of waste. People wore masks, not so much to protect against infections, but to block "bad air" and odors. As a hospital nurse during the Crimean War in the 1850s, and based on her belief in miasma, Florence Nightingale famously campaigned for fresh air, cleanliness, and other hygiene measures.[19]

Knowledge of the Germ Theory Revolutionized Medical Practice

By the end of the 1800s, "germs" were finally accepted in the U.S. as the agents causing the infections. Based on knowledge of the cause of infections, scientists began making breakthroughs in the fight against infections. Development of the germ theory was based on the work of scientists such as Antoine van Leeuwenhoek, Robert Koch, Louis Pasteur, and Joseph Lister. Unfortunately, in the 1890's, sanitation measures were the best and only strategy for prevention of infectious disease.

A breakthrough in the discovery of the germ theory was Van Leeuwenhoek's invention of a high-powered microscope in 1642 that could magnify objects up to three hundred times their size.[20] With the use of a microscope, Koch could identify bacteria in tissue. He was able to demonstrate to other scientists that bacteria caused anthrax and tuberculosis. In 1867, Joseph Lister published his *Antiseptic Principle of the Practice of Surgery*.[21] He strongly advocated that to prevent germs, cleanliness during surgery was vitally important to the subsequent recovery of the patient. He used carbolic acid to clean wounds and instruments, and one study noted a decrease in death rates from infectious disease from 60 percent to 4 percent due to following his procedures. Knowledge of the germ theory revolutionized medical theory, medical research, and medical practice. The germ theory of disease provided a sound scientific basis for public health.

In Europe, the theory that germs rather than miasma were the cause of infections was widely accepted as early as the 1860s.[22] However, U.S.

clinicians and researchers continued to believe in the concept of noxious miasma until the 1880s. Even Florence Nightingale initially believed that infections were due to "poisonous air." She believed that scarlet fever, measles, and smallpox were caused by odors coming from the drains built below houses. It was not until 1882, when Robert Koch published his discovery of the tuberculin bacillus,[23] that Florence Nightingale and U.S. researchers finally accepted that germs were the cause of infectious diseases.

Due to the Civil War, the medical community in the U.S. was focused on the immediate needs of providing care for patients, rather than changing their practices due to studies from abroad. The reluctance to accept the germ theory in the U.S. had deadly consequences. In London in 1857, Dr. John Snow reported that cholera was due to contaminated water.[24] In the U.S., however, instead of focusing on unclean water and separating water supplies from sewage disposal, public health experts focused their energies on poisonous air and odors. Thus, U.S. lives were lost from cholera that could have been saved if we had accepted that germs in the water were causing cholera.

Causation and Spread of Infectious Diseases

Prevention of the cause and spread of infections requires more than just an understanding that germs cause disease. Infection control also requires knowledge of which germs cause certain diseases and how these germs are spread. The following paragraphs include information about specific germs that cause disease, how these germs are transmitted or spread, and what factors make some individuals more susceptible to diseases.

Germs such as bacteria, viruses, parasites, and fungi are the agents that cause infectious diseases. These tiny germs have made a powerful impact on the history of the world. Tuberculosis, typhoid fever, cholera, and dysentery are caused by bacteria, and smallpox, measles, and influenza are caused by viruses.

Causes of Infection: Bacteria and Viruses.[25] The most important distinction between bacteria and viruses is that antibiotic drugs usually kill bacteria, but they are not effective against viruses. Bacteria are single-celled organisms and antibiotics can effectively destroy bacteria by attacking their cell walls.

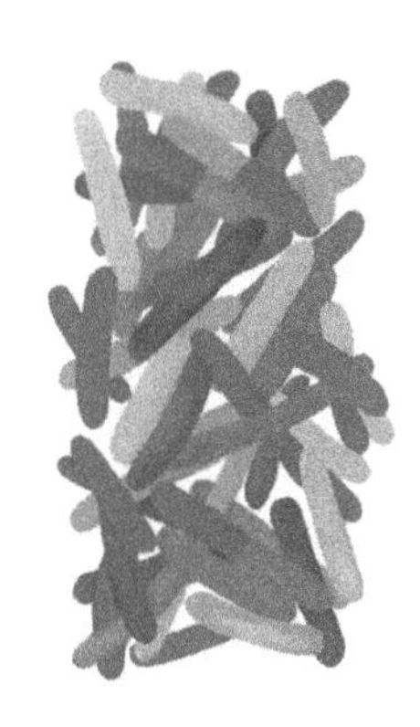

Bacteria
TB, typhoid fever, cholera, dysentery Bacterial rods in picture depict TB bacterium Illustration by Erica Parker Rogers.

Bacteria are living organisms that can live inside or outside human or animal hosts and can reproduce on their own. They are so small that a thousand of them end to end could fit on the end of a pencil eraser. Ninety-nine percent of bacteria are not harmful, and some are quite necessary for humans. Bacteria called *Lactobacillus Acidophilus*, for example, live in the human gut and are vital for digestion.

Most viruses cannot live outside of animal, plant, or human hosts. Spikes on the viral globe are used to attach to specific cells on the host. When viruses attach to cells, they hijack and re-program the cells to make more viral cells. Generally, the original cells burst and die.

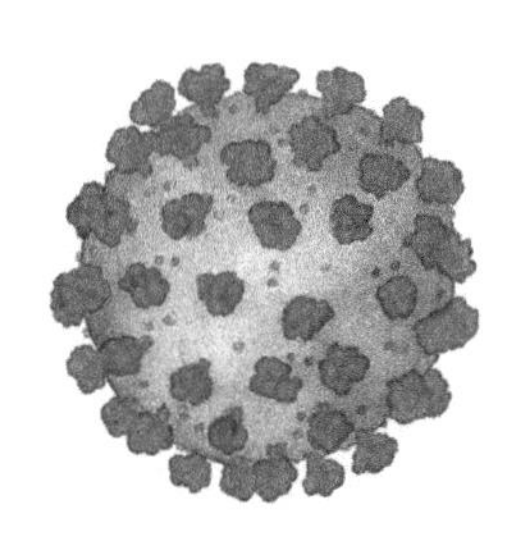

Viruses
Influenza, smallpox, measles. Illustration by Erica Parker Rogers.

The viral globe is covered with a strong, protective protein coat, and the inside of the sphere is made up of a genetic code of nucleic acids consisting of RNA and DNA. Viruses are even smaller than bacteria, and most viruses are potentially harmful.

Mostly because of their protective protein coating, infections caused by viruses have been incurable in the past. The belief was that most viral infections, such as the common cold, were benign and resolved without treatment. Unfortunately, viral infections have been a leading cause of death in humans since the beginning of time. Currently there are antiviral drugs that are effective in treating viral infections, although the treatment may not be curative. These drugs work, not so much by attacking the virus's protein coating, but by preventing the formation and replication of the RNA and DNA inside the viral capsule. The most effective management of viral infections, however, is prevention with the use of vaccines.

Spread of Infections: Zoonotic Diseases. Infectious diseases that can jump from animals to humans are termed "zoonotic" diseases.[26] Zoonotic diseases that will be discussed in later chapters include tuberculosis and influenza. Tuberculosis (TB) can spread from cattle to humans. Some humans have developed TB from drinking the milk of infected cows. Influenza in humans can originate in birds or animals. Generally, birds become contaminated with the virus, spread the virus to animals, and then animals spread influenza to humans.

According to the readings, most infectious diseases first occurred in animals and then jumped over to humans. Thus, smallpox and measles, at least at one point in time, were zoonotic diseases. Dogs can develop canine distemper from a virus that looks like the measles virus in humans. However, there is no evidence that, at present, dogs cause measles to humans. Some infections are spread from horses to humans. However, horses will not spread any of the diseases covered in this book. Good handwashing is obviously important after caring for any animals.

Preventing the spread of infections. One of the primary goals for infection control is to prevent the spread or transmission of these infectious agents. Germs can spread through the air, through contact with others and with surfaces, from animal and insect bites, and by consuming contaminated food and water. TB and influenza are spread through the air, especially from coughs and sneezes. Measles and smallpox can be spread through the air and by close contact with infectious sores or bodily fluids.

Dysentery, typhoid, and cholera are not airborne diseases. Rather, they are spread by feces in food or water that enter the mouth. Thus, infected food handlers should not be working with food. All food handlers should wash their hands thoroughly after using the bathroom and before touching food. All communities should have safe water supplies and effective systems for sewage disposal. Flies can carry germ-laden feces and spread diseases such as dysentery by landing on food and eating surfaces.

Sanitation procedures, such as hand washing, the wearing of face masks, ensuring clean food and water, isolating infected patients, and the cleansing of all surfaces that have had contact with germs are critical for preventing both bacterial and viral infections.[27]

Susceptibility of the Host. Some patients are less able to fight off infection when exposed. Historically, Native Americans had not been exposed to many of the infections occurring in Anglo Americans. Thus, they had no "host" immunity. Native Americans who were older in age, had underlying diseases such as alcoholism or TB, or were malnourished were much more likely to develop other infectious diseases and to die from them.

Susan La Flesche's Role in Promoting Sanitation

When she began her practice at the boarding school and on the reservation, Susan observed multiple problems in sanitation. These included lack of handwashing, poor ventilation, no screens to prevent the entrance of mosquitoes and flies, no isolation of the sick, and tribal members drinking from a communal drinking cup. She believed that there could be contamination from human feces, and that families could be drinking contaminated water and eating spoiled food.[28]

During an address to the Women's National Indian Association, Susan was quoted as saying; "*As a physician, I will help the Omaha's physically, teach them the importance of cleanliness, order, and ventilation, and how to care for their bodies as well as care for their souls*"[29].

As an Advocate for Public Health

In the early 1900s, there were an increasing number of scientific studies supporting public health and sanitation measures to prevent infections. Susan promoted a constant message that "*Sanitation Equaled Prevention.*"[30] Sadly, Susan La Flesche's advocacy for public health was frequently opposed, often by leaders of her own community.

When Susan first practiced medicine, her time was spent providing medical care for her patients. Later in her life, she spent more time advocating for her people and promoting legislation to help her people. Susan was a member of the Nebraska Medical Society. Also, many of Susan's greatest contributions in public health were a result of her role as chair of the state health committee of the Nebraska Federation of Women's Clubs (NFWC). In 1908, the NFWC called for more aggressive action in the field of public health. They focused especially on food sanitation, personal hygiene, school hygiene, social hygiene (sex education), and the prevention of TB. Susan believed that public health began at the grass-roots level, with education. This meant cooperating with school and county boards to organize Health Days. She believed that exhibits, booklets, and wall cards should be available to the public at schools and at city and county agencies.[31]

Susan launched impassioned campaigns to educate her people about the need for sanitation, the need to stop the practice of multiple people drinking from the same cup (the communal drinking cup), and the use of screens to rid homes of the common house fly. She told her people to avoid crowding two or three generations into single, poorly ventilated homes, where one ill person could easily infect everyone else.

She encouraged all tribal members to scrub their hands often with soap and water—especially after toileting and before preparing or eating food. She instructed her patients with infections to use separate wash-basins and hand towels. All people in her practice should be covering their mouth when coughing or sneezing. Healthy diets (high in vitamins, minerals, and fiber) and fluids should be encouraged along with regular exercise and sleep.

Susan lobbied for all Native American children at the government school to be examined monthly for TB. In addition, she asked for routine medical inspection of schools, for sanitary ice cream dishes and spoons, for school drinking fountains, and for the establishment of a playground for reservation children.

Susan fought throughout her career to educate her patients both about TB and alcoholism. Her special focus was always on TB. In 1907, she wrote to the Office of Indian Affairs (OIA) about the growing problem. In her letter she stated "*The spread of TB among my people is something terrible. So many of the young children are marked with it in some form. The physical degeneration in twenty years in my people is terrible,*"[32] On National

Tuberculosis Day, Susan spoke at local churches, and her addresses were published in the newspapers to reach a wider audience.

Susan also described the problem of eye infections such as trachoma with the OIA. As a result, some changes were made in the boarding schools. In 1895, for example, roller-towel systems were condemned in the schools because of the danger of spreading trachoma. Susan made trips to Washington, D.C., to advocate for public health measures. She organized the Thurston County Medical Association and served on Walthall's Health Board. She consistently fought for building a hospital on the reservation both for treatment of the seriously ill, to assist women having complications with delivery during childbirth, and to isolate patients with infectious diseases. Her dream became a reality in 1913.[33]

Throughout history and before antibiotics and vaccinations, infectious diseases were deadly for Native Americans. Chapters six, seven, and eight will describe Susan La Flesche's challenges in providing medical care to her patients with life-threatening infectious diseases that have devastated Native American populations.

SIX

Tuberculosis

Seven of the life-threatening infectious diseases that have caused death and destruction in Native Americans and the Omaha people were TB, influenza, smallpox, measles, typhoid fever, cholera, and dysentery. Chapter six describes the disease "TB" and examines its impact on the Omaha tribe and on the practice of Dr. La Flesche.

Tuberculosis (TB): The Greatest Killer in History

TB has been described as one of the deadliest diseases throughout history, claiming more lives than any other diseases.[1] TB has been present "*as long as humans have walked the earth.*"[2]

Presentation, Causation, and Spread.[3] Patients with TB suffer from fevers, night sweats, shortness of breath, pain, and they are tired 100 percent of the day. They lose weight even when trying hard to keep their weight on. They have a chronic cough, and often cough up blood. In the 1800s, people suffering from TB were often called "lungers" because the disease commonly affected the lungs. While over 85 percent of TB patients have infection in the lungs, TB infection can also occur in areas such as the spine ("Potts" disease), brain, and kidneys. When patients are "lungers," the infection is generally spread to others through the air.

TB has also been called the "the "graveyard cough" or "consumption." In the movies, such as *Moulin Rouge*, the tragic heroine coughed up blood into her lacy handkerchief, and this was the clue that told the audience that the heroine was going to die. Thus, since TB has been associated with coughing up blood, this disease has been called the "graveyard cough." TB is one of the few infectious diseases that can be chronic, and over time, patients lose weight and waste away.[4] In the past, *"TB patients were so weak that they were consumed by other diseases that swooped in like vultures. This explains why consumption was another name for TB."*[5]

The germ causing TB is a bacterium named "*Mycobacterium TB*."[6] The disease is spread through the air, often through coughs or sneezes. In the 1800s, there were several TB epidemics in Anglo Americans, and one reason for this was the movement of Americans from rural to urban areas. In urban areas, there was poor sanitation, overcrowding, and patients with TB were not isolated.[7] TB could be spread by infected persons spitting on sidewalks and streets. Alcoholism and poor nutrition contributed to the high incidence of TB. Fortunately, TB is not as contagious as other respiratory diseases such as measles and influenza.[8] Patients with chronic TB, however, can infect many other people over the years.

Doc (John Henry) Holliday (1851–1887)
Dentist, gambler, and gunfighter. Died of chronic TB. Shuttlestock.

Doc Holliday and Chronic TB. Few readings have described the tragic quality of life for patients with chronic TB before the development of antibiotics. An excellent description of chronic TB in the late 1800s has been found in readings on the life of the infamous gun fighter, Doc Holliday.[9]

Doc Holliday, born in 1851, was a part-time dentist, a gambler, and a gunslinger. He developed TB at the age of twenty-one, lived with his disease for fifteen years, and finally succumbed from the illness at the age of thirty-six. He was most famous for participating in the gunfight at OK Corral along with his friend, Wyatt Earp. Doc survived the gunfight but could not survive TB.

Doc Holliday's full name was John Henry Holliday, and he was born in 1851 to an aristocratic southern family in Griffin, Georgia. When he was fifteen years old, his mother died of TB, and historians believe that Doc may have developed TB from his mother. At the age of twenty-one, while practicing dentistry in Georgia, he started to lose weight. Six months later, in 1873, he developed a nagging cough. His uncle, Dr. John Stiles Holliday, diagnosed him with pulmonary TB, and the uncle recommended that Doc leave hot and humid Georgia and move west to a drier climate.

Doc moved to Dallas, Texas, and continued to practice dentistry. Besides his unstoppable coughing spells tinged with blood, Doc was tired, had fevers, was depressed, lost weight, and had severe pain. The pain was caused by incessant coughing, irritated nerves, fractured ribs, and ruptured lung tissue. To control the pain, Doc used Laudanum, whiskey, and an herbal treatment consisting of bugleweed. Bugleweed (*Lycopus virginicus*) is a common weed and herb in North America that can be used as a sedative or a mild narcotic. It was used in the nineteenth century by patients with TB to relieve the pain of a blood vessel rupture or bleeding into the lung.

Some of the best first-person accounts of Doc Holliday were written by the gunfighter "Bat Masterson," who later became famous as the sheriff of Dodge City, Kansas. Masterson wrote that Doc was so physically weak that he could not have even whipped a healthy fifteen-year-old boy in a fight. Consequently, Doc developed his talents as a gambler and gunfighter. In 1884, Doc's condition began to deteriorate into stage 2 TB. He had mental confusion, lost consciousness, and died in Glenwood Springs, Colorado, in 1887. His last comment to his nursing attendants was that he never expected to die this way. He expected to lose a gunfight somewhere along the way and to die with his boots on.

The History of TB. Between 1600 and 1900, TB killed 20 percent of the world's population.[10] Emily Bronte, Frederic Chopin, Vivien Leigh, Eleanor Roosevelt, George Orwell, President Andrew Jackson, Tina Turner, Nelson Mandela, Cat Stevens, Ho Chi Minh, Ringo Starr, and Desmond Tutu have all had TB.[11]

In the late 1800s, by studying its spread in rabbits, Robert Koch was able to prove that air-borne bacteria caused TB.[12] Koch's discovery, along with the works of other researchers, led to the building of sanitariums for TB to isolate patients as well as to provide patients with fresh air and open spaces. The first sanitarium was built in 1875. While sanitariums did not necessarily cure TB, patients in sanitariums did receive better care and other people were prevented from developing the disease.

TB and the Omaha Tribe. In the 1700s, Omaha people were nomads, and typically did not have prolonged exposure to others. This all changed with the influx of Anglo-American populations into their territory and with resulting changes in U. S. policies. Instead of living a nomadic life in the rural prairies, the U.S. government forced Native Americans to move to crowded reservations. People on the reservations were frequently exposed to TB and had little resistance once infected.

TB has devastated hundreds to thousands of Native Americans. In the 1860s and 1870s, one-quarter of Omaha people on the reservation contracted some type of infectious disease every year, and the main causes of death were from tuberculosis and pneumonia.[13] At the beginning of the 1900s, TB was the most serious health problem among the Omaha people. Unfortunately, before knowledge of the germ theory, leaders of the OIA believed that TB was hereditary, and that Native Americans were predisposed to dying from TB.

Susan dedicated much of her life to reducing the risk of TB in her Omaha patients. She consistently emphasized the importance of "healthy food, rest, outdoor living, fresh air, sunshine, and exercise," both for the prevention and treatment of TB. These practices continue to be recommended today. Healthy food, rest, and exercise bolster the immune system. Fresh air and outdoor living reduce the spread of TB to others. Susan fought for years against the "communal drinking cup" because she recognized that the cup was a carrier of TB.[14]

Many of Susan's friends and family had developed TB, and her first love, an American Indian named Thomas Ikinicapi, died of TB.[15] Susan taught her patients the sanitation and public health measures for TB described in chapter five, and she encouraged patients to have adequate nutrition and avoid alcohol.

> *On one visit, she saw a young girl lying on the floor who had attended the Hampton Institute—the same educational school Susan had attended prior to medical school. The girl had suffered from TB for over a year, had now developed the flu, had not eaten for four days, and her breathing was soft and shallow. Every day for two weeks, driving her buggy in the snow, Susan visited her patient, bringing and cooking food such as milk, eggs, and beef, and often spending the night with her patient. As frequently happened with TB, the young girl died.*[16]

Susan's brother-in-law, Charles Picotte, and her husband, Henry, were also victims of TB.[17]

During the 1880s, medical schools offered little education on end-of life care, because most patients who were seriously ill died within days or weeks. Susan had no formal education on needs of dying patients. Yet she knew to remain with patients and families during the time of a patient's death. She stressed that dying patients should be offered fluids and nutrition, if possible. Susan advocated for comfort measures, and she administered medications for pain and anxiety. She spent additional time comforting families of dying patients.

Vaccine and Treatment Today. Albert Calmette, a French physician, and Camille Guerin, a French veterinarian and bacteriologist, did develop a vaccine to prevent tuberculosis, the BCG vaccine. While not as effective in older children and adults, the vaccine appears to offer some protection from TB in infants. Some countries worldwide continue to administer the BCG vaccine to infants.[18]

In 1943–1944, an American scientist, Selman Waksman, discovered the antibiotic "streptomycin" which, at least initially, could effectively cure TB. With this discovery, most sanitariums closed. Unfortunately, resistance against streptomycin developed, and this one drug was not curing enough of the patients. Currently, triple antibiotic therapy is used, where three antibiotic drugs are administered together over time. Antibiotics are administered over six to nine months, and in some cases, use of these drugs may be continued over several years. Antibiotic drugs used are commonly isoniazid, rifampin, and ethambutol.[19]

Over the six months, the patient is monitored for toxicity using blood tests, and most often the concern is toxicity to the liver. The importance of patients with active TB taking these drugs cannot be overstated. The spread of TB from patients endangers families and communities. If there is any concern that patients are not taking the drugs, Direct Observed Therapy (DOT) is recommended. With DOT, patients are observed taking their drugs, and observers are clinic nurses or other trustworthy personnel.

Many people who are infected with the TB bacterium carry the organism but never develop symptoms of TB. These people who have "inactive" TB cannot spread the disease. They may develop "active" TB later when they are older, weaker, or have another illness, however. Currently, for selected populations at risk, screening tests such as the Purified Protein Derivative (PPD) skin tests are used to detect the presence of TB infection in patients, even though they have no symptoms. Patients with positive PPD tests receive lung x-rays, and positive x-ray results are diagnostic for active TB. Even with inactive TB, patients must take six to nine months of the antibiotic "isoniazid" (INH) to prevent active TB from developing later. During the six to nine months, these patients are also monitored for hepatic (liver) toxicity.[20]

Unfortunately, TB is still very much a problem in the U.S. and throughout the world. Worldwide, 4100 people die from TB every day. It also has been estimated that currently up to 40 percent of new cases of TB are unreported and undiagnosed. Without treatment, TB will kill 45 percent of its victims.[21]

Also, more of the TB presenting today is resistant to most antibiotics. With multi-drug resistance, there is a real danger of more TB deaths in the future in the U.S. and elsewhere. The Bill Gates foundation has committed their future funding to more research on management of TB.[22]

SEVEN

Influenza, Smallpox, and Measles

Chapter seven is devoted to three other deadly infectious diseases that have plagued Native Americans over the centuries: influenza, smallpox, and measles.

Influenza (the flu): More Deadly than the Common Cold

Influenza has had tragic results for Omaha people and all Native American populations for centuries. Most people who are infected do survive the flu. However, because the flu is so contagious and so many people become infected, flu epidemics can be extremely deadly. The Italians coined the word "influenza," for this epidemic meaning "a blast of stars." This word is appropriate because influenza epidemics are so sudden and widespread in their impact.

Presentation, Causation, and Spread.[1] Patients with the flu complain of a cough, sore throat, and runny nose, and they can be misdiagnosed as having a common cold. If they also have a high fever, muscle aches, headaches, and feel extremely ill, however, they have the flu. The onset of the high fever is sudden, and patients often remember the exact time when the fever occurred and when they started feeling ill. A deadly complication of the flu is pneumonia. The pneumonia can be from the flu virus or may be a secondary bacterial infection. Besides the lungs, the heart, brain, and muscles can be involved Patients who are most likely to die from the flu are the very young and the very old, pregnant women, and patients who have TB or other chronic diseases.

Influenza is caused by rhinoviruses and is spread through the air. There are four types of rhinoviruses that can cause the flu: A, B, C, and D. Type C is rare, and this type does not cause epidemics. Type D affects cattle and pigs. Types A and B affect humans, birds, and animals. Humans are now annually vaccinated against both types A and B. Influenza A is the most concerning because its symptoms are more severe.[2]

When Christopher Columbus and his men came to the New World in 1492, the crew suffered from fever, lung problems, and were just feeling ill. Columbus and his men were most likely infected with the flu. Included in the Columbus expedition were pigs, horses, and hens acquired in the Canary Islands, and they may well have been the original carriers of the flu. According to John Barry, who authored *The Great Influenza*, all of influenza should be called the bird flu, because the virus never first occurs in humans. Birds are the storage places for the flu, and they spread the virus to other animals, especially pigs. The virus in pig (swine) flu has been found to be genetically close to the virus in humans. "*The most dangerous places on earth are anywhere people, birds, and swine are crowded together in large numbers.*"[3]

History of Influenza. The first flu epidemic was believed to have occurred in 1173. Patients had all the symptoms of the flu. However, their diagnosis cannot be certain because accurate records were not kept. The first reported flu epidemic was in 1694, and since that time, flu epidemics have occurred on a regular basis. Since the 1600s, there have been at least thirty widespread epidemics that have resulted in a considerable number of patient deaths, and four of the deadliest epidemics occurred in 1918 (Spanish flu), 1957 (Asian flu), 1968 (Hong Kong flu), and 2009 (swine flu). [4]

Spanish Flu of 1918

The "1918 Spanish flu" is considered the deadliest worldwide plague since the Middle Ages.[5] *Epidemic* is derived from the Greek word for "upon the people," and is generally not spread worldwide. Pandemic is a disease extending across the world in a dramatically short period of time. The "1918 Spanish flu" was a pandemic. An estimated two billion people were stricken, and 20 to 40 million people worldwide died from the Spanish flu, far more than all the deaths in both soldiers and civilians that occurred during World War I.[6] Approximately 600,000 to 700,000 people In the U.S. and one out of every 100 people on earth died due to this pandemic.

During the "Spanish flu," posters were visible in most villages and cities throughout the world advocating social isolation, good handwashing, and wearing masks. Wearing masks when in public was required in many U.S. states and cities.[7] Schools were closed, shops were closed, and hospitals were overflowing with patients. Unlike most flu epidemics, the Spanish flu caused illness and deaths in a disproportionate number of young people. The death rate from the Spanish flu was so overwhelming that it was impossible to bury all the corpses. Dead bodies were stacked because grave diggers couldn't keep up. Abandoned buildings were used as morgues.[8]

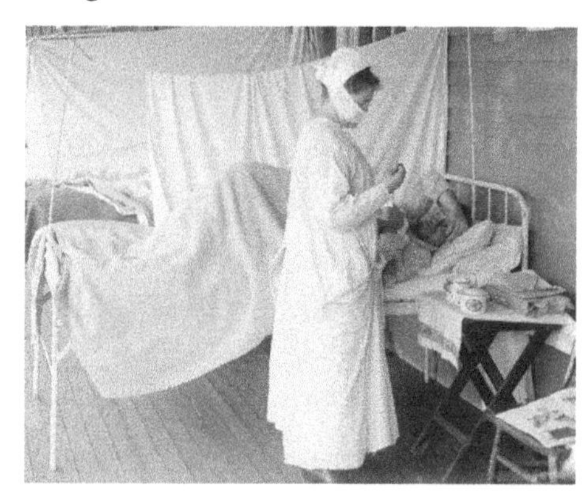

1918 Spanish Flu
Walter Reed Influenza ward
Shuttlestock.

The strain of flu virus that attacked in 1918 was particularly nasty. Patients would be admitted coughing up blood, their breathing was labored, and their skin had a blue-black cast.[9] In hospitals, men and women would be admitted with what appeared to be an ordinary attack of the flu. By the second day, the lungs had been transformed from an oxygen-rich "sponge" to a bloody "rag." The patient would literally drown in his or her own fluids. "*One patient showed his first symptoms at 4:00 pm and died at 10:00 am the next day.*"[10] Deaths were generally due to pneumonia and respiratory and heart failure.[11]

The following are first-hand accounts of survivors of the Spanish flu. "*Bustling major cities and rural towns were brought to their knees, as transportation, law enforcement, commerce, and civic life were wiped out." "That was the roughest time ever. Like I say, people would come up and look in your window and holler to see if you were still alive. They would never come in because of fear of getting infected."*[12]

In 1919, President Woodrow Wilson was a victim of the Spanish flu. He developed the flu during the Paris Peace Conference; he was still recovering from the flu when he negotiated the World War I peace treaty—the Treaty of Versailles. According to the readings, President Wilson never did regain his physical, mental, or emotional strength after his episode with the flu.[13]

The Spanish flu appeared to occur simultaneously in many parts of the world within a dramatically brief period. Experts now believe that the "Spanish" flu did not originate in Spain. The exact origin of the Spanish flu remains controversial. It appears to have originated at World War I military installations and may have started in the U.S. According to this theory, the flu originated in Camp Funston, which is part of Fort Riley, Kansas. Camp Funston is near Haskell, Kansas, which housed up to 40,000 World War I soldiers. Haskell, Kansas, was a small rural town, and inhabitants in this area raised both pigs and chickens. Over 1,100 people in Camp Funston contracted the flu. Camp Funston also hosted several English and French officers who could have spread the virus when they returned to Europe. The flu also spread from Camp Funston to a boarding school for Native American children near the present town of Lawrence, Kansas. A week after the outbreak at the camp, the school was drowning in sick children, and their hospital wards were overflowing.[14]

In 1918, there was no accurate system for reporting incidences of diseases. In addition, in the U.S. and worldwide, sanitation was poor. There were few organized efforts to ensure sanitation procedures such as hand-washing and clean water. As a result of experiences during the Spanish flu, our government greatly expanded services of the U.S. Public Health department.[15]

Influenza and the Omaha Tribe. In 1918, numerous Omaha people had the "Spanish" flu and were admitted to the Walthill hospital on the Macy reservation. Over fifty people from the Omaha tribe died at the hospital. There wasn't room in the hospital morgue for all the bodies, and they had to be shipped elsewhere.

Influenza was the most serious illness on the Macy Reservation in the 1800s, and flu epidemics occurred annually and often in the winter. During the very cold and icy winter of 1891, two flu epidemics occurred on the Macy Reservation, and during these two epidemics, Susan treated more than 140 patients.[16] Patients often lacked fluids and nutrition and were extremely weak. She wrote that often every member of the family except one or two were infected. Although there were no fatalities among adults, two babies died.

Susan never failed to visit her patients with the flu, even though making home visits exposed her to the cold and to icy roads. In December 1891, with temperatures at fifteen and twenty degrees below zero, she was still making house calls. Susan cared for one man who was so ill that the family did not expect him to live, and Native American medicine had not been helpful. She gave him fluids and medicines for fever and cough, and he rallied around. In a few days, he had recovered.

Susan was aware that the flu was spread through air or by hand contact with droplets on objects such as towels. She knew that the Omaha people with the flu were contagious for five to ten days (about one and a half weeks). She encouraged isolating ill patients for as long as they had a fever or symptoms, good hand washing, and frequent cleaning of objects that may contain contagious droplets. Medications were needed to reduce fever. Susan also emphasized that people with TB, older people, and pregnant women should be especially careful to isolate themselves from people with the flu.

Vaccine and Treatment Today. The most important strategy for the prevention of flu and its severe outcomes is annual vaccination against seasonal flu. Flu vaccinations are highly recommended for all individuals and are required for special populations of individuals. Flu vaccines have been available since the 1940s. However, as with many rhinoviruses, flu viruses mutate (change) as they reproduce, and viruses are slightly different with every new season. Thus, different mixtures of viral flu vaccines must be administered annually. Typically, vaccines consist of some mixture of both A and B type viruses.[17]

In addition to vaccines, antiviral drugs play a key role for patients who have not been vaccinated, are at increased risk of complications, or who do not respond to vaccines. Today, there are at least four antiviral drugs available for the treatment and prevention of the flu, and the most common antiviral drugs used are oseltamivir (Tamiflu) and Zanamivir (Relenza). Prescribing antivirals is most effective when the patient has only had the flu for twenty-four to forty-eight hours, or less than two days.[18]

In the 1890s, patients who developed complications of the flu, such as pneumonia, often died of their disease. Today, these patients are hospitalized and would have access to treatments such as intravenous fluids and antibiotics and continuous oxygen. Of course, these were not available for the Omaha people in the 1890s.

Throughout history millions of people have died from the flu. Even today, in the U.S. alone, 30,000 to 49,000 people die every year from the flu. Unfortunately, the public is not as fearful of seasonal flu infections as they are of other diseases. Many Americans do not even get annual flu vaccinations, even when offered locally at a low cost or no-cost. Vaccinations offer moderate to large protection against the flu and probably for more than one year.

The most likely cause of a major catastrophe that would result in millions of people worldwide dying every year would not be a war or a hurricane; the most likely cause would be a pandemic of an infectious disease, most likely viral, and potentially a flu pandemic. One infectious disease introduced in 2020 that has been deadly for millions of people worldwide has been caused by the infamous COVID-19 virus. Dr. John Hultin was a San Francisco physician who spent much of his life studying the deadly viral variant that caused the 1918 Spanish flu. According to Dr Hultin, a killer virus can reappear again at any time. He is quoted as saying, "*It isn't 'if' a killer virus comes back, it's when.*"[19]

Smallpox (The Speckled Monster): The Disease Most Feared by Native Americans

Historically, the infectious disease most feared by Native Americans was not TB or the flu but smallpox (caused by the *Variola minor* or *major* virus). The name smallpox came about because victims of smallpox had pox marks on their face and body. However, the markings were smaller than those left by syphilis, which was known as large pox or French pox. Although smallpox was eliminated from the earth forty years ago, for many Native Americans, smallpox remains one of the scariest monsters on earth. Throughout history, over a billion people have suffered and died from smallpox, and billions more have been permanently scarred or disabled.

Presentation, Causation, and Spread.[20] Ten days after contracting the virus, patients with smallpox had symptoms such as back pain, headache, fever, nausea, and vomiting. As soon as symptoms appeared, patients could infect others. After about the fifteenth day, a pox rash appeared. The rash often started in the nose and mouth and then spread to all parts of the body. Eventually, poxes burst and scabbed over. Over this time, patients had immense pain. The heart, lungs, kidneys, and liver could stop working. By day thirty, if patients were still alive, they would often be scarred for life, but they would no longer be contagious.[21]

There were two types of smallpox—variola minor and variola major. With variola major, the very young and very old were less likely to survive. Pregnant women had a 96 percent chance of dying. Even if people survived, they could have long-term problems such as blindness and scar tissue. Between 65 and 85 percent of survivors were left with pox marks or scarring, commonly on the face. Women in the 1700s and 1800s were praised if they had fair skin—meaning they had no scarring from smallpox. Men often hid scarring with full, bushy beards.[22] Too often in the 1700s and 1800s, if Native Americans survived smallpox but had unsightly scarring from the disease, members of their tribe shunned them.

The smallpox virus was spread through the air by a cough or sneeze, by direct contact with infected persons, and possibly even through contact with these person's clothing. The virus was extremely contagious but could only be spread by humans. Animals had their own type of pox diseases, including cowpox, which could be present in cattle.[23] Often, one person with smallpox infected ten to twenty other people. Also, while most viruses are extremely fragile and cannot survive outside of the human host, the smallpox virus was more durable. Rarely, some smallpox viruses have survived up to one year outside of a dead body.[24] One of the reasons that smallpox was so feared in the 1700s and 1800s was because the virus was still alive even after the infected patient had died. Undertakers refused to touch people who died from smallpox. Instead, dead bodies were buried by using ropes to drag them to graves. Clothes and blankets of patients with smallpox were burned to destroy any remaining viruses.

The Incident at Fort Pitt.[25] In 1763, British soldiers at Fort Pitt, Pennsylvania, deliberately attempted to spread smallpox to the Ottawa tribe of Native Americans by giving them contaminated blankets. The militia commander, William Trent, wrote to his superior that he had sent the Ottawa people "two blankets and a handkerchief out of the smallpox hospital" with the aim of spreading the disease. The suggestion for this hateful action came from Field Marshal Jeffery Amherst.[26] The prestigious Amherst college in Massachusetts was named after him.

There have been other references over the years of U.S. military personnel intentionally spreading smallpox to rid the nation of Indians. However, none have been as well documented as the incident at Fort Pitt. Although the attempt at Fort Pitt did occur, there is no evidence that Ottawa people did develop smallpox from these blankets. There is controversy as to whether providing blankets of smallpox patients would even be a successful method for spreading smallpox.

The History of Smallpox. Smallpox is believed to have been brought to America, not by Christopher Columbus in 1492, but by Hernando de Soto in 1518.[27] in the 1500s, smallpox caused the death of fifty percent of the Timucuan tribe in Florida, from a population of 722,000 to 361,000.[28] In 1639, the disease killed about half of the 20,000 members of the Huron-Wendat community.[29] Native Americans infected with smallpox often died because they were already malnourished and frail. So many members of the tribe had taken ill that there were few left to care for the recovering victims of smallpox.

Smallpox and the Omaha Tribe. Lewis and Clark reported in their journals about a smallpox epidemic that struck the Omaha tribe in the winter of 1800 to 1801. They estimated that the epidemic caused the death of more than half of the tribe.[30] This same epidemic took the life of the leader of the Omaha tribe, Chief Blackbird.

In 1832, the United States implemented a vaccination program for all Native Americans, and the vaccinations saved the lives of multiple Omaha people. However, not all Native Americans were vaccinated, and not all vaccines were quality vaccines. Unfortunately, smallpox disease continued to stalk tribal people for many years after vaccinations had become available.[31]

In her practice, Susan would have encouraged strict isolation for patients infected with smallpox, and vaccination for all members of the tribe who had not been vaccinated. Unfortunately, there was no treatment for the disease beyond making the patient comfortable.

The Smallpox Vaccine. Historically, while 33 to 45 percent of patients with variola major died from their illness, only 2 to 10 percent of patients with variola minor died. Also, symptoms of variola minor were generally milder. By the 1700s, physicians had recognized that no one got smallpox twice. They also knew that patients who contracted variola minor were less likely to die from their smallpox. Thus, scientists began to experiment with the practice of variolation.[32] Physicians would inoculate or inject patients with a small amount of variola minor. Patients would then need to self-isolate for four weeks and would most likely be ill, but they had less chance of dying. During the American War of Independence in 1776, George Washington mandated that all members of his army be inoculated using the technique of variolation. Washington's mandate worked. Men in his army did not develop smallpox, and Washington defeated the British.[33] Unfortunately, variolation was not without its dangers. Some patients could become very sick, and some would even die from the technique.

In 1796, Edward Jenner discovered the technique of vaccinating against smallpox using cowpox, and by the 1800s this vaccination had spread around the world.[34] By 1900, most Americans had been vaccinated for smallpox. However, even as late as the 1960s and 1970s, smallpox was killing three million people a year.[35] in 1956, the World Health Organization began efforts to vaccinate people worldwide against smallpox.

The last case of smallpox was recorded in 1978 in Birmingham, England, and occurred in Janet Parker, a forty-year-old medical photographer.[36] Janet had been photographing slides in the smallpox laboratory at the Birmingham Medical Center. This medical center was one of less than twenty in the world that still had a smallpox laboratory. Unfortunately, Janet contracted the virus at the lab and died from the infection. Initially, she had a rash and fever. Before long, she became partially blind due to sores around her eyes. Days later, she developed pneumonia and was no longer able to respond verbally. One month after she first showed symptoms, Janet Parker died, becoming the world's last smallpox victim.

Janet's body was not refrigerated for fear of spread of the virus. She was kept in a transparent body bag, and workers were shocked by the horrific sores and scars that appeared—even after her death. Janet was cremated to prevent any further chance of spreading the virus. The ward at the hospital where she died was sealed off for five years. The head of the smallpox laboratory at the medical center, Dr. Henry Bedson, committed suicide. According to his suicide note, he ended his life because he was so ashamed that smallpox infection had occurred in his laboratory.[37]

Because of this occurrence, the World Health Organization now only allows two laboratories in the world to continue to store smallpox samples—*one laboratory in the U.S. and one in Russia. Samples at all other institutions were* destroyed. In 1980, smallpox was declared eradicated (eliminated) from the world. "*To this day, smallpox remains the only major infectious disease that humans have successfully eradicated.*"[38]

Measles (Rubeola): Not Just a Disease of Children

Historically, measles has been common in infants and young children. However, too often, the seriousness of developing measles has been underestimated. The disease can be deadly for people at any age. While some patients consider measles to be a mild disease, it can be profoundly serious for many individuals, especially if they are immunocompromised.

There are two types of measles, rubeola and rubella. Although the types appear alike (red rash and fever), they are caused by two different viruses. Rubeola (standard or hard measles) is much more severe than rubella, and is the measles described in the following discussion. Rubella is often called German or 3-day measles and tends to have milder symptoms. Rubella, however, can be severely damaging for unborn babies (fetuses) when mothers become infected during pregnancy.

Presentation, Causation, and Spread.[39] Patients with measles (rubeola) have a high fever (sometimes a temperature of 103° or 104° Fahrenheit); severe episodes of coughing; inflamed, reddened eyes that are sensitive to light; a severe runny nose; and headaches. They are extremely tired and have a red rash. The rash often first occurs on the face, and Koplik spots (small bluish-white dots) can be seen on the inside lining of the cheek.

Complications of measles can include middle ear infections and hearing loss, scarring of the eyes and blindness, inflammation of the brain (encephalitis), and lung infection (pneumonia).[40] Pneumonia is the most common cause of death. Before the development of vaccines, measles was the leading cause of blindness in children.[41]

Measles (rubeola) is caused by the *Measles morbillivirus*[42] and is spread through the air. Also, the virus can live up to two hours on hard surfaces and can be spread through contact with these surfaces. Measles is more deadly than most other childhood diseases, and the measles virus is more contagious. Ninety percent of those living with a person infected with measles will get the disease.[43]

The History of Measles. The three most deadly diseases for Native Americans that were introduced by the European explorers were smallpox, measles, and influenza. "*Mortality rates from the newly introduced diseases were estimated to be between 60 and 95 percent.*"[44] For example, in 1524, the Timucuan tribe in Florida were infected with smallpox and lost half their population. Four years later, the measles pandemic caused the death of another half of the population.

Measles and the Omaha Tribe. Since the 1500s, epidemics of measles among all Native Americans, including the Omaha people, have occurred approximately every two years.[45] In 1888, there was a terrible scourge of measles on the Macy Reservation. Eighty-seven tribal members had died—mostly children.[46] Susan La Flesche had not yet obtained her medical degree and was overwhelmed by what she saw. Many of her people were mourning the loss of children and were in serious need of care and food. Even though she was not yet a doctor, she treated the sick and dispensed food. From her long buckboard wagon rides visiting families, she saw how many patients on the reservation needed medical care and the help of a trained physician.

When Susan received word of an outbreak of measles on the reservation, she knew that she would be treating multiple people. Whole families would have the measles, and the disease would have spread to numerous families on the reservation. As a doctor, Susan would encourage her patients with measles to rest and drink plenty of fluids. They may need treatment (possibly an herbal treatment) for a fever and to relieve a cough and sore throat. Patients with measles often found bright lights bothersome, and she would encourage them to rest their eyes. She would encourage patients to isolate themselves from others until all symptoms were absent or relieved.

Susan knew that people who were malnourished were at higher risk of developing measles complications. One vitamin, Vitamin A, has been identified as especially important for preventing eye problems in measles patients.[47] As she often did in her treatment of patients, Susan recommended adequate nutrition. For Vitamin A, that nutrition would include eggs and milk as well as vegetables such as potatoes, carrots, and squash·

There are fewer measles outbreaks in reservations today because Native American children are being vaccinated. However, from January 4 to May 13, 1985, a total of 114 cases occurred on the Blackfeet reservation in northwest Montana, and most occurred in school-age children. None of the eighty students at the reservation who were vaccinated at less than twelve months of age and revaccinated at fifteen months of age or older became infected.

Vaccine and Treatment Today. In 1963, Drs Katz, Enders, and Peebles developed the first safe and effective vaccine for measles.[48] The vaccine is now in a required immunization package for children in developed countries. Two doses of the vaccine are required in children, one when the child is twelve to fifteen months old and the second shot when the child is four to six years old. In addition, vaccination is highly recommended for all U.S. citizens returning from overseas and for travelers from overseas without documented proof of adequate immunization or measles immunity.

Unfortunately, measles continues to survive worldwide and the U.S. In 2013, there were 145,000 reported deaths worldwide from the disease. In the U.S., there was an outbreak of measles in Disneyland at California in 2015. The disease sickened 147 people in the U.S., including 131 people from California. The outbreak was believed to be caused by unvaccinated children from other countries who visited Disneyland. Measles diagnoses increased in the U.S. both in 2017 and 2018. In 2019, there were seventy-one measles cases reported in Clark County, Washington.[49]

The World Health Organization, Pan American Health Organization, and the Centers for Disease Control convened a meeting in July 1996 to consider the feasibility of global measles eradication or elimination worldwide. The belief was that since smallpox has been eliminated worldwide, measures should be taken to eliminate measles. Even though a safe and effective vaccine is available, this disease continues to remain one of the leading causes of both blindness and death among young children, especially in countries outside the U.S. This virus could be eliminated worldwide if more people were vaccinated. The major obstacles to vaccination are not technical but perceptual, political, and financial.

Some people are choosing not to vaccinate their children because they have been misled to believe that vaccinations cause autism. In 1998, a report in the British journal *Lancet* claimed a possible link between the measles vaccine and autism. The report was later debunked as fraudulent and the author, Dr. Andrew Wakefield, lost his medical license.

Measles is often mistakenly perceived as a mild illness. This misperception inhibits the development of public and political support for the allocation of resources to finally eliminate measles. The disease burden imposed by measles should be documented, particularly in industrialized countries, so that this information can be used to educate parents, medical practitioners, public health workers, and political leaders about the benefits of eliminating measles forever.

EIGHT

Typhoid Fever, Cholera, and Dysentery

In all three of these diseases—typhoid fever, cholera, and dysentery—germs are present in human feces (stool). Infection occurs when the germs in the feces are spread to the mouth either by eating contaminated food or drinking contaminated water. Epidemics of typhoid fever, cholera, and dysentery can all be prevented if basic sanitation procedures and public health measures are in place. During her time with her patients, Susan consistently promoted prevention of infections from contaminated food and water. She taught her patients good handwashing (especially after toileting and before and after eating food). Patients who were ill should be using separate towels and wash cloths, and if possible, should not be preparing food. She encouraged patients to screen their windows to prevent flies from entering food areas. She discouraged the practice of patients drinking water from a communal cup. She advocated for clean water and for drinking fountains in the schools.

Typhoid Fever: The Four Fs: Feces, Food, Fingers, and Flies

Typhoid fever is another of the deadly infectious diseases brought to America by European explorers. Causes of typhoid have been labelled the "*four F's: feces, food, fingers, and flies.*"[1]

Presentation, Causation, and Spread.[2] Symptoms of typhoid can be mild to severe and usually begin six to thirty days after exposure. Typhoid fever has been known as "burning fever" or "slow fever" because there is a gradual onset of high fever (103° to 104° Fahrenheit). Other symptoms include weakness, abdominal pain, diarrhea or constipation, headaches, and vomiting. Patients may develop a skin rash called "rose spots," which are small red spots on the abdomen and chest. Bacteria in patients with typhoid can spread through the blood and lymph system to the stomach and intestines, spleen, liver, and gallbladder.

In severe cases, bloody stools, agitation, confusion, delirium, and even hallucinations can occur. The word "typhoid" comes from the Greek word for "foggy" and refers to the fever and mental condition of patients with typhoid.[3] If the patient survives, the disease generally runs its course in one to three weeks. If complications occur, the disease can be fatal. Death can occur from Intestinal perforation, an overwhelming blood infection, and failure of the heart, kidneys, and lungs. Without antibiotic therapy, typhoid has a mortality rate of 10 to 30 percent.[4]

Salmonella bacteria cause typhoid fever, and many epidemics occur because feces that are harboring *Salmonella* have entered the water supply.[5] Sewage containing typhoid contaminate well water. Patients who carry *Salmonella* and prepare food can contaminate others, and this is often because they are not washing their hands adequately. Flies often carry feces to water and food. Typhoid fever can only be spread from human to human. However, when there are a lot of animals in an area, such as dogs, horses, pigs, and cattle, there are more flies. With more flies, there are more chances for flies to land on human feces and spread contamination. In 1847, although he had no knowledge of *Salmonella* bacteria, William Budd of Clifton, England, was the first to discover that patients developed the disease from drinking water from the same well. The bacterium *Salmonella* was identified as causing typhoid fever in 1880 by Karl Eberth and George Gaffky.

"Typhoid Mary" Mallon (1869–1938).

Approximately three to five percent of patients with typhoid fever have the bacteria in their feces after their acute infection, and often for a lifetime. These people have no symptoms; however, they may continue to infect others. Unfortunately, in the past, many of these "asymptomatic" carriers were working in the food industry.[6] Mary Mallon was an immigrant from Ireland who worked as a cook and is believed to have been responsible for between 55 and 122 cases of typhoid fever. In the summer of 1906, she was hired as a cook by a wealthy New York banker named Charles Henry Warren. Warren had a family of four and seven servants. Mary was an excellent cook, and the family loved her "peaches on ice" dish. However, Mary left their employment abruptly, supposedly to work elsewhere. A few weeks after she left, six of the ten remaining people in the Warren household were stricken with typhoid fever.

George Soper, who had a PhD in engineering and was known as a "germ detective" provided the evidence implicating Mary Mallon as the carrier of typhoid and cause of the infection in the Warren family.[7] Mary continued her practice of working as a cook and leaving when she was suspected of carrying infection. Even after she had been confirmed as a carrier of typhoid, she refused to quit her job as a cook. She never believed she was a carrier and was rumored to be mentally ill. She is quoted as saying, "*It's ridiculous to say I'm dangerous.*"[8]

Finally, after putting up a fierce resistance, Mary was arrested. She kicked and screamed and attacked the officers with a meat cleaver. In 1915, she was forced to quarantine in a cottage in North Brother Island in New York City, and remained alone, except for her dog, until she died in 1938. At the end of her life, George Soper admitted that "*the world was not very kind to Mary.*"[9]

Typhoid Mary was not the only healthy carrier of typhoid. By the time, Mary died in 1938, there were 4500 cases of typhoid fever in New York City annually, and four hundred healthy typhoid fever carriers had been registered. In 1933, the American Medical Association recognized that carriers of typhoid bacilli could be a danger to society. When recognized, carriers were instructed on how to dispose of excreta (stool) and on the importance of personal cleanliness. They were forbidden to handle food or drink intended for others, and their movements and whereabouts were to be reported to public health officers.

As of 2018, chronic typhoid carriers must receive antibiotic treatments and then sign "Carrier agreements" requiring them to be tested for typhoid shedding at least twice yearly. Typhoid shedding is tested with fecal and urine specimens. Since the bacteria harbor in the gallbladder, if antibiotic treatment is not successful, the gallbladder can be surgically removed. Gallbladder removal may or may not be effective in preventing people from being carriers; bacteria in some cases appear to be also harbored in the liver. Research is currently being conducted to determine why some individuals can tolerate infections for long periods of time without having symptoms, and to determine the most effective ways these individuals can be identified and treated.

History of Typhoid. Typhoid fever came to America with European explorers, most likely Christopher Columbus in 1492.[10] Between 1607 and 1624, 85 percent of the Native American population at the James River near Richmond, Virginia, died from a typhoid epidemic. The World Health Organization estimates the death toll was over 6,000 during this epidemic.

Due to lack of proper sanitation, contaminated water, and poor sewage systems, typhoid fever was common in army posts during the Civil War.[11] Typhoid fever occurred, even though in army hospitals a post surgeon was assigned to make certain the water supply was adequate and clean, the latrines were kept in sanitary order, and the garbage was properly disposed. Physicians at the time often treated typhoid by "purging the bowel" or "use of enemas." Of course, this left the patient in a worse condition.[12.]

Throughout the seventeenth, eighteenth, and nineteenth century, typhoid fever epidemics had been frequent and deadly. Numerous famous people have died from typhoid including Abigail Adams, wife of U.S. President John Adams,1818; Steven Douglas, political appointment of Abraham Lincoln,1861; William Lincoln, son of Abraham Lincoln,1862; and Wilbur Wright, builder of the first successful airplane,1912.[13]

One of the cities in the old west in the mid-1800s labelled as "filthy" due to poor sanitation was Omaha, Nebraska.[14] Water supplies were contaminated, and garbage and sewage flooded the streets. One epidemic of typhoid fever occurred in Omaha in 1874. The problem was that most Omaha citizens had an outhouse or privy in their back yard. Although citizens of Omaha were told to follow sanitation procedures, most people living in Omaha did not practice sanitary cleaning of privies. They usually just provided openings in the rear of the outhouse, and sewage and waste freely ran out into the soil. The soil contaminated with feces found its way into local water supplies. Privies attracted dogs, rats, hogs, horses, and other animals that wallowed in the filth of the feces. While horse and other animal feces did not carry *Salmonella*, their feces did attract more flies to the city, and flies carried the infected human feces to foods. In 1945, a law was passed prohibiting the use of privies in the city proper. With the invention of the automobile, fewer horses were on the streets of the city, and this also improved the fly and pollution problem.

Two epidemics of typhoid fever occurred in Lincoln, Nebraska, in 1911 and 1912. Lincoln had a population of about 45,000. There were three wells providing water to the city, and a well-developed sewer system. Unfortunately, leakage of the sewer pipes resulted in contamination of the well water. A thorough review was conducted, and the sewer system and pipes were repaired.[15]

The first attempts to clean the water supply by adding chlorine to the water occurred in 1893 in Hamburg, Germany. In 1897, Maidstone, England, was the first town to have its entire water supply chlorinated. The first permanent disinfection of drinking water in the U.S. was made in 1908 in the Jersey City, New Jersey, water supply.

Today, the highest cases of typhoid occur in Southeast Asia and Sub-Saharan countries. During the Vietnam War in the 1960s, American soldiers drank water from a Lyster bag hanging from a pole. Chlorination tablets had been added to clean the water in the bag. Since the 1900s, most developed countries have had declining rates of typhoid due to vaccinations and advancements in public sanitation.[16]

Typhoid Fever and the Omaha Tribe. There is little documentation of episodes of typhoid fever among the Omaha tribe of Native Americans at the time of Susan La Flesche, although the disease was present in Nebraska. In contrast, dysentery, which is also caused by human feces entering the water and food supplies, has frequently been reported on the Macy Reservation.

When Susan cared for typhoid patients, there were not antibiotics available to treat typhoid. Susan would encourage adequate fluids, and patients with typhoid would need to be isolated. Susan was a strong advocate for clean water supplies and effective systems for removal of sewage and feces. More information on preventing the spread of feces to food is included in the next sections on cholera and dysentery.

Vaccine and Treatments Today. A vaccine was developed for typhoid by Almoth Wright in 1896. The first patient in the U.S. to be vaccinated was Frederick Russell in 1909. Currently, two vaccines are available, one oral and the other an injection. Vaccinations are recommended for all people in areas where typhoid is endemic, and for all U.S. citizens who travel to an underdeveloped country. Vaccines can prevent about 40 to 90 percent of cases during the first two years, and they may have some effect for up to seven years. Booster doses of oral vaccines are recommended every five years, and for the injectable vaccine, every two years.[17]

Starting in 1999, the World Health Organization endorsed a vaccination program for all people in underdeveloped countries. However, vaccination programs alone cannot eliminate typhoid fever. Public health efforts along with vaccinations are necessary to control this disease. In 2015, 12.5 million new cases of typhoid were reported worldwide.

Treatment for typhoid includes antibiotics such as the fluoroquinolone "ciprofloxacin" or the third generation cephalosporines such as ceftriaxone or cefixime. Treatment with antibiotics reduces the case fatality rate to about 1 percent. One concern in health care today is that in some areas of the world *Salmonella* is becoming resistant to antibiotics. With the concern of drug resistance, vaccinations become even more critical in preventing epidemics of typhoid.[18]

The Devastation of Cholera in the Frontier West

Cholera was one of the most notorious infectious diseases in the frontier west, and the spread of the infection was primarily through contaminated water. Major cholera epidemics occurred in the U.S. in 1837, 1849, and 1866, and the spread was typically among large concentrations of people. Cholera was common in pioneers on wagon trains traveling along the Oregon and Mormon Trails to California and Oregon. In the early 1840s and for twenty-five years afterward, 400,000 to 500,000 pioneers emigrated west along the 2000-mile trails. The number one killer on the trails, by a wide margin, was infectious diseases, and the most common infectious disease was cholera.

Presentation, Causation, and Spread.[19] Cholera is an infection of the small intestine caused by various strains of the bacterium *Vibrio cholerae.* Cholera bacteria have been found in shellfish and plankton, but this cause of cholera was not observed in the frontier west. The strain of cholera most damaging in the Nebraska Territory was "Asiatic cholera."

Generally, spread of Asiatic cholera is due to untreated diarrheal discharge that contain cholera bacterium getting into waterways, groundwater, or drinking water supplies. People develop cholera from drinking contaminated water or from eating foods washed in the water. Most cholera bacteria would not survive the journey through the acidic conditions of the human stomach. However, the few bacteria that do survive move toward the walls of the small intestine. Here they colonize and produce toxic proteins that cause the watery diarrhea.

Severe white watery (rice-like) diarrhea is the classic symptom of cholera, along with vomiting of clear fluid and muscle cramps. Patients with cholera can produce three to five gallons of diarrhea a day. "Cholera" is a Greek word for roof gutter. The name is appropriate because the diarrhea in a patient with cholera is like drain water gushing from a gutter.[20]

Patients with cholera die from dehydration, kidney failure, and electrolyte imbalance. Because of the diarrhea, blood sugar and blood potassium are at dangerously low levels. The blood pressure drops, the pulse becomes rapid and thready urine output decreases, and the kidneys fail. Eventually, patients lose consciousness, or develop seizures. One frightening aspect of cholera is the speed at which it kills. Patients can die in two to twenty-four hours after the development of symptoms. If cholera is not lethal in the first twenty-four hours, the disease typically runs its course in five to seven days, and the patient survives. Without treatment, about half of people with severe cholera die of their disease.[21]

The Father of Epidemiology and Public Health—Dr. John Snow.[22] For years the spread of cholera was a medical mystery. Up to the mid-nineteenth century, medical scientists believed that cholera was spread through bad air or "miasma." In 1854, London was in the middle of their worst cholera outbreak ever. One English physician, Dr. John Snow, after caring for multiple cholera patients, came to a different conclusion. He believed that cholera was spread by contaminated water. He had observed that many of his cholera patients were using the same water supply. To confirm his belief, he conducted a study in a West End neighborhood of London—the Soho district. He chose this district because within ten days of a diagnosis of the first case of cholera, five hundred people in the area had died. This number of people was over 10 percent of the population. Dr. Snow started collecting and analyzing data describing specifically the areas where cholera was occurring. He developed a "ghost map" showing concentrations of patients in specific areas. After analyzing his map, he concluded that most of the cholera cases occurred in people who were getting their water from the Broad Street pump. However, even with all the overwhelming evidence Dr. Snow presented, the General Board of Health in London was not convinced enough to shut down the pump.

With the assistance of Reverend Henry Whitehead, a curate at John Snow's church, Dr. Snow continued his investigation and found "patient zero," the first person to die of cholera in the 1854 outbreak. This person was the baby daughter of Thomas and Sarah Lewis, who lived near the Broad Street pump. Sarah Lewis placed the infected baby's diapers in water tor washing, and then threw out the dirty water into a cesspit a scant three feet away from the pump. Within days, numerous cases of cholera had developed around the neighbor's home. With this new evidence, and Reverend Whitehead's encouragement, the Board of Health excavated the cesspit and reconstructed the pump. Because of his efforts at data collection and analysis, Dr. John Snow is now considered the Father of Epidemiology and Public Health.

Tragically, Dr. Snow's discovery was not accepted by the "medical experts" in the U.S., who continued to believe in the "miasma" theory for another thirty years. Medical clinicians in the U.S. did not accept "germs" as causing disease until 1882, when Robert Koch identified the tuberculin bacillus under a microscope.

The History of Cholera. Cholera was believed to be present in India 2,000 years ago. However, Cholera first appeared in the spring of 1832 in the U.S. in New York. From there, it spread rapidly throughout the U.S. and eventually moved westward. The first reported cholera epidemic in the U.S. was in 1849 in Chicago. During this epidemic, 678 people died of the disease.[23]

James K. Polk, the eleventh president of the U.S. died of cholera in 1849. He was a very popular president during his four-year tenure. Under Polk, the U.S. defeated Mexico in the Mexican American War, and a million square miles of land was added to present day California. Polk had promised to resign after serving only one term, and stepped aside for Zachary Taylor to become the twelfth president of the U.S. Soon after Polk resigned from office, he and his wife travelled the Mississippi River on a tour of the southern states. Unfortunately, he developed cholera in New Orleans, and died from his illness.[24]

Cholera along the Oregon Trail.

Many of the outbreaks of cholera in Nebraska occurred in the 1840s, 1850s, and 1860s among emigrants traveling the Oregon Trail. Emigrants traveled west along the trail hoping to find free and fertile land for farming or to mine for gold that had been found in California. The beginning points for the Oregon Trail were Independence or St. Joseph, Missouri, and the end points were Oregon or California. This 2000-mile migration is considered the largest land migration in our country's history. The Oregon Trail united the coasts, doubled the size of the economy, and laid the groundwork for the transcontinental railroad.[25]

The path for the Oregon Trail was developed by the most famous chart-making explorer of the time, Captain John C. Fremont. Congress appropriated $30,000 to pay for the expeditions and surveys that would map the path along the Trail, and Fremont was selected to head the expeditions. Between 1842 and 1853, he and his men conducted five expeditions to explore the west. The 1842 trip was significant for Nebraska history because it outlined the Platte Valley South route that passed through Nebraska as the most useful for most California- and Oregon-bound emigrants.

Fremont hired a guide to help him with his expeditions, an American frontiersman, wilderness guide, and Indian agent named Kit Carson. Carson later became a frontier legend, mostly because of exaggerated versions of his exploits that were the subject of numerous dime novels. Nebraska owes its name to Fremont; in his report to U.S. leaders, Fremont called the great central river on the trail (the Platte) by its Native American name "Nebraska," or "Flat Water." The U.S. Secretary of War then suggested that Nebraska would be a good name for the new territory.[26]

John Charles Fremont (1813–1890)
Explorer and Mapmaker. Nebraska State Historical Society Photographic Collections.

Fremont loved the west and the Nebraska Territory and believed that easterners would be pleased with their travels. He saw the Platte River Valley as a garden with rich soil, abundant grass, and beautiful wildflowers. He believed the valley would be the best path for emigrants to follow. The valley was warm much of the year, the land along the river was flat, and there was water to drink, fresh game, and tinder for cooking fires.

Unfortunately, by the 1850s, mudholes along the Platte were filled with human and animal waste and sewage. The water in the Platte River was so muddy that it was undrinkable. Thus, pioneers dug in the mud holes to find water that tasted good enough to drink. Between the five or six travelers in the wagon and the multiple oxen or mules, every wagon on the train would require numerous gallons of water a day. When wagons moved away from the rest stops, people and animals would leave their sewage and waste in each mud hole, and future travelers would develop cholera. As a result, thousands of travelers along the trail succumbed to cholera between 1840 and 1865.

One letter sent by an emigrant on the trail told of the devastation of cholera; "*I would like to mention the sickness we have had, and I am sorry to say the deaths. First, Francis Freel died June 4,1852 and Maria Freel followed on the 6th. Next came Polly Casner, who died on the 9th, and LaFayette Freel's death soon followed. He died the 11th, and her baby died the 7th. So you see, we have had a sad affliction on our short journey. We have lost 7 persons in a few short days; all died of cholera."* [27]

Even though deaths in the Platte River Valley were common, emigrants also enjoyed the wonder of the scenery. Many pioneers wrote that they would travel the Oregon Trail again if necessary. Writers remarked about the beauty of the Platte River Valley, the romantic terrain, and the majesty of Courthouse Rock, Jail House Rock, and Chimney Rock. The Nebraska towns now present along the trail are Kearney, North Platte, and Scottsbluff.

Painting by William Henry Jackson: Approaching Chimney Rock, SCBL-25
Depicts wagon trains on the Oregon trail in the Platte River Valley. Jackson (1843–1942) was a photographer, veteran, painter, and explorer, famous for his images of the American West. Born in New York, he served in the Civil War, and took part in the Battle of Gettysburg. Later, he lived in Omaha and acted as "missionary to Native Americans" in the region around Omaha. He is buried in Arlington Cemetery. The largest collection of his paintings is at the Scotts Bluff National Monument in Nebraska. Courtesy of Park Service, Scottsbluff National Monument and Museum

Cholera and the Plains Tribes of Native Americans.[28] In the 1800s, cholera outbreaks devastated Plains tribes. Proportional losses in Native

Americans far outweighed those of white communities. Documentation of losses in Plains tribes due to cholera are extremely sketchy. While there is no information available, it is almost certain that many Native Americans from the Omaha tribe died of cholera. The Commissioner of Indian Affairs wrote that "*How many thousands of Plains Indians died in this cholera disaster cannot be known.*"[29]

The Indian sub-agent at Council Bluffs reported in October 1849 that 1,234 Pawnee or nearly one-fourth of the tribe died of cholera in the space of five or six months.[30] Indian agents on the Upper Missouri wrote that smallpox, cholera, and measles had so thinned the tribes' ranks that the Native Americans talked constantly about the people who had died.[31]

At the Council Bluffs agency, wolves partially devoured corpses of Native Americans found near a Pawnee village.[32] Members of the Comanche tribe became so weakened with cholera they didn't even have the strength to bury their hundreds of dead. Three to four hundred or one-fourth of the Osage tribe perished from the disease. Similar stories were told of the impact of cholera on many other tribes, including the Apache, the Shawnee, the Delawares, the Mandans, the Arikaras, and the Hidatsas.[33]

Many Native Americans traded with the Anglo Americans along the Oregon trail, and the Native Americans who traded with the whites were more likely to develop cholera. Diseases like cholera hardened nomadic tribes and left them more willing to retaliate against the whites.

A Native American from the Kiowa tribe was quoted as saying, "*We were sorry later that we permitted the white travelers to go through the plains. They brought us two terrible diseases, smallpox, and cholera, which killed half our people. Some of us thought that they gave us these sicknesses on purpose to wipe us out.*"[34]

The sudden and explosive nature of cholera epidemics horrified white doctors as well as the traditional Indian healers. Patients were treated by encouraging fluids to compensate for the loose stools. The most common error doctors could make would be not to administer enough fluids. A recipe for fluids would include one liter of boiled water, ½ teaspoon of salt, and 6 teaspoons of sugar. The patient would have lost potassium in the diarrhea. If bananas were available, they could be eaten to replace the lost potassium.

Oranges or berries would also work. One concern is that many patients would not be able to drink enough fluids to keep them alive. The administration of intravenous therapy with salt-water solutions to treat cholera patients was introduced by Dr. Thomas Latta from Edinburgh, Scotland in 1832. Dr. Latta's treatment saved many lives. However, intravenous therapy was not widely used in the United States until the 1920's and 1930's.

Vaccine and Treatment Today. The first vaccine for cholera was developed in 1885. Today, there is both an oral and an injectable vaccine available. Neither vaccine however provides long-term protection. The World Health Organization suggests that an oral vaccine such as Vaxchora could be administered in areas where the disease is endemic and as part of a response to outbreaks. People traveling from the U.S. to endemic countries could also take the oral vaccine. Although these vaccines are only effective for a short period of time, they have reduced outbreaks of cholera in endemic countries.

In addition to vaccines, between the mid-1850s and the 1900s, cities in developed nations have made vast improvements in ensuring clean water supplies and well-separated sewage treatment programs. In 1972, The U.S. government passed the Clean Water Act mandating that cities maintain wastewater treatment plants.[35]

Today, patients with cholera are treated with intravenous therapy. The preferred solution for infusion is Ringer's Lactate with the addition of potassium. Zinc supplementation has been effective in treating children with cholera. Zinc appears to reduce the length of the disease by eight hours and the amount of diarrhea stool by 10 percent. There is a high incidence of secondary bacterial infections such as pneumonia with cholera, and antibiotics are also used today to shorten the disease and reduce severity of symptoms. The first effective antibiotic for cholera was developed in 1948. Antibiotics that are used are typically doxycycline, azithromycin, tetracycline, and ciprofloxacin.[36] In many parts of the world, however, antibiotic resistance to treatment of cholera has developed, and that limits the choice of antibiotics that can be used. Fortunately, because of improved treatment, only 5 percent of patients infected die from their disease. Without treatment, mortality rates continue to be about 50 percent.

Cholera continues to affect an estimated three to five million people worldwide and causes 28,800 to 130,000 deaths a year in undeveloped countries. Although there are periodic outbreaks, cholera is not as common or as deadly in the U.S. This is because cities now have well-developed water systems, more effective treatments, and they practice judicious use of vaccines. [37]

Dysentery: Loose Stools and More

Throughout history, dysentery has been the most common infectious disease of the bowel. Dysentery has also been a major cause of death in the 1700s and 1800s, and frequently occurred in the Omaha tribe at the time of Susan La Flesche. Deaths from dysentery were equal in numbers to smallpox, measles, influenza, and typhoid fever. Like typhoid and cholera, dysentery is contracted by ingesting food contaminated with feces or by drinking, bathing in, or swimming in water containing feces.

Presentation, Causation, and Spread.[38] Symptoms of dysentery include violent diarrhea with blood, pus or mucus, severe stomach cramps, and extreme tiredness. There can be internal bleeding, breakdown of the Intestinal wall, dehydration, and weakness that results in survivors being susceptible to other diseases. Because of its symptoms, dysentery has been commonly known as "flux" or "bloody flux."

Generally, symptoms only last five to seven days. However, dysentery can be chronic or greater than thirty days and symptoms can be intermittent. At times, the abdominal pain appears to be relieved; however, it often comes back again. Death is generally due to dehydration and the Inability of the immune system to protect the patient from other illnesses.

Before antibiotics, some people suffered for long periods of time before dying, while others suffered for short amounts of time. There was no timeline for symptoms and recovery with dysentery as there was with smallpox and measles. One patient described a chronic case of dysentery as the following. "*I felt slightly ill for two to four weeks . . . I was reduced to extreme weakness, so that I could not walk without pain or effort. . . . I could hardly keep my seat on horseback. My symptoms continued for several years, and I never fully recovered.'*[39]

Dysentery can be caused by a number of organisms, although most commonly it is caused by gram-positive, rod-shaped bacteria such as *Shigella*[40] or by a protozoan called *Entamoeba histolytica*. Susan La Flesche treated the bacterial form of dysentery. The protozoan dysentery traditionally occurs in the tropics.

It is important to note that not all diarrhea (the frequent and uncontrolled expulsion of watery feces) is dysentery. However, when the diarrhea is severe, greater than six stools per day, when there is a high fever, generally 102° or greater, and when stools are grossly bloody, the diagnosis is most likely dysentery.[41]

History—Dysentery During the Civil War. The magnitude and severity of dysentery infections in the 1800s were best described in records kept during the Civil War.[42] Diarrhea and dysentery were constant features of army life, and most cases were not even entered into the records. Dysentery was often known as "camp fever" or "camp disorder." Soldiers called dysentery the "*Virginia Quickstep*" or the "*Tennessee Trots*."[43] Dysentery, when acute and short-lasting, was responsible for few fatalities during the war—only 1.7 percent. However, when soldiers were dehydrated and when there were severe nutritional deficiencies, dysentery could become chronic. Fatality for chronic dysentery was higher than for acute dysentery and accounted for 23 percent of deaths due to infectious diseases.[44] During the Civil War, personal hygiene was poor and water systems were contaminated. Meals during the Civil War were lacking in nourishment. They included small portions of hash, stew, baked beans, salt pork, coffee, and bread.[45] In addition, army doctors had no treatment for dysentery. Most commonly, soldiers were treated with opium, quinine, and brandy.[46]

In addition to cholera, incidences of dysentery were common on the Oregon trail. Often, the disease was related to emigrants drinking water from holes dug in the riverbank and along marshes.[47]

Dysentery and Omaha Tribe. Dysentery was quite common on the Macy Reservation because it was so contagious, there was overcrowding, sanitation was poor, water was contaminated, and there were no organized systems for disposal of sewage. Omaha tribal people could be infected with dysentery for weeks or years with no symptoms and could pass the infection to others.

Susan La Flesche encouraged her patients with dysentery to wash their hands frequently and to drink lots of fluids. Anyone exposed to dysentery should not be preparing food, sharing towels, or drinking cups, and feces should be properly disposed of. Symptom management may have included the use of opium, Laudanum, and Paregoric to lessen diarrhea. Susan may also have prescribed a Native American herbal treatment for stomach disorders consisting of chewing the root of a plant called sweet flag (*Acorus calamus*). Native Americans even mixed sweet flag into the feed of horses who were ailing.[48]

Vaccine and Treatment Today. Today, antibiotics such as fluoroquinolones (ciprofloxacin) can save lives in people suffering from dysentery from bacterial causes.[49] At present, there are no vaccines effective in in preventing *Shigella* infections. However, research is ongoing to develop the vaccines.[50]

Due to improved public health and sanitation practices, dysentery is not as widespread in the U.S. or on Native American reservations as previously. However, especially in underdeveloped countries, dysentery remains a leading cause of death in children. Each year, some 760,000 children under age five die from diarrheal diseases, and dysentery is one of the top four causes for these diseases. *Shigella* is the bacterium responsible for two-thirds of these dysentery cases. One concern is that *Shigella* infections are becoming more resistant to the common antibiotics used for treatment.

The Centers for Disease Control provides the following recommendations for anyone in areas where there are concerns about the development of typhoid, cholera, or dysentery.[51]

- Drink only water that has been boiled or disinfected.
- Avoid ice, unless there is certainty it has been made from safe water.
- Eat food that has been thoroughly cooked and still hot when served.

- Avoid raw seafood or raw produce rinsed with unsafe water.
- Boil unpasteurized milk.
- Ice cream from unreliable sources may be contaminated.
- Meals bought from street vendors should be thoroughly cooked in your presence.

NINE

Historical Trauma

During her medical practice, Susan became increasingly concerned about depression in the Omaha tribe and the alcohol abuse on the reservation. She believed that liquor had degraded the Omaha people. With alcohol, she observed immorality in a notably moral tribe. Throughout her lifetime, Susan tried to understand the cause of alcohol abuse in her tribe and to find ways to prevent this abuse. Chapter nine describes historical trauma, or "trauma of the soul," as one of the causes of alcohol abuse and other health and behavioral problems in Native Americans today.

Compared with all other racial groups in the U.S., Native Americans are more likely to have poorer overall physical and mental health and to have a lower life expectancy. In 2020, "*26 percent of Nebraska Indians perceived their health as only fair or poor.*"[1] Alcohol abuse continues to be a significant mental health problem. In 2020, it was estimated that deaths in one out of eight Americans were either directly or indirectly related to alcohol; compared to all other races, Native Americans had even higher death rates from alcohol.[2]

Historical Trauma or "Trauma of the Soul"

Some theorists have associated health problems and addictions in Native Americans to a "trauma of the soul." The premise of this theory is that *"populations subjected to long-term mass trauma exhibit a higher prevalence of disease even generations after the original trauma occurred.*"[3] To quote the American writer William Faulkner, "*The past is never dead. It's not even past.*"[4]

In addition to Native Americans, historical trauma is believed to be a cause of health problems in populations subjected to slavery and in populations where genocide has occurred, such as the Jewish communities in World War II. The theory of historical trauma was first developed by Maria Yellow Horse Brave Heart in the 1980s, while she was working with Lakota Sioux communities. Yellow Horse Brave Heart described how the traumas over generations of colonization, relocation, assimilation, and federal boarding schools have impacted the Sioux population even today.[5]

In the 1500s, thousands of Native Americans died from infectious diseases such as smallpox and measles, brought to them by European explorers.[6] In the 1700s and 1800s, policies of the U.S. government resulted in tragic results for Native American populations. Confinement to reservations culminated in their loss of land and poverty, malnutrition, and illness. Native American men confined to reservations were not able to provide for their families. This led to disruptions in the family structure and to "learned helplessness" as families became dependent on goods provided by the U.S. government. U.S. policies of forcing Native Americans to become civilized or to "assimilate" to white culture resulted in distrust of Anglo Americans and to "trauma of the soul." The following is a "Chronology of Events" describing selected interactions between the Native Americans and the U.S. government.

Chronology of Selected Events Impacting Relations between U.S. Government and Plains Tribes: 1700–1900

1775 **Legislation from Second Continental Congress**

The government assumed control over all Native American tribes in the U.S. This decision was not intended to be a detriment to the lives of Native Americans. However, this action resulted in confinement of many tribes to reservations, including the Omaha people to the Macy Reservation, hundreds of years of fighting between tribal people and whites, and heartbreak that ended the Native American way of life.

1803 **Louisiana Purchase_**

President Thomas Jefferson purchased over 500 million acres (including the Nebraska Territory) from Napoleon Bonaparte of France.

1804 **Lewis and Clark Expedition**

Lewis and Clark were commissioned to explore Louisiana Territory and find the safest path through the territory to the Pacific Ocean. The Lewis and Clark Journals no doubt hastened the voyages of white settlers from the east to the great unknowns in the west.

1819–1969 **Indian Civilization Act**

Federal Boarding Schools were mandatory for Native American children in thirty-seven states to "*civilize the Indians.*" The schools were created to strip away cultural ties in Native American children and force assimilation to the Anglo-American culture.

1854 **U.S. Treaty of 1854**

Peace treaty signed between U.S. and Plains tribes confining Native Americans to reservations.

1862 **Homestead Act**

Signed by Abraham Lincoln, provided 160 acres of free public land in the west to "whites" who agreed to settle on the land. As a result of the Homestead Act an increased number of white settlers came to the Nebraska Territory. White traders and buffalo hunters came with the settlers, and herds of buffalo began to diminish.

1869 **Completion of the Transcontinental Railroad_**

Central Pacific Railroad from the West was connected to Union Pacific from the East ensuring travelers a safe

	route from the Atlantic to the Pacific. The railroad was a major cause of the near eradication (elimination) of the of the buffalo as well as the loss of the land and the lives of a devastating number of Native Americans.
1870	**Plains Indian Wars of post-Civil War Era_** The beginning of the worst years of warfare between the U.S. and Plains tribes of Native Americans.
1871	**Warren Wagon Train Raid** A brutal and deadly attack by Kiowa tribe led by Satanta on wagon train carrying food and supplies to forts in Texas.
1876	**Battle of Little Big Horn** Sioux tribe led by Sitting Bull defeated 7th Cavalry in southern Montana.
1878	**Trial of Standing Bear** Decision of trial that took place in Omaha, Nebraska was that Native Americans should have the same rights and freedoms as Anglo Americans.
1887	**The "Dawes" or "General Allotment" Act** U.S. legislation was passed encouraging individual initiatives in Plains Native Americans and was aimed at breaking up tribes as social units.
1890	**Massacre at Wounded Knee** Over two hundred Lakota Sioux women and children were needlessly shot to death by U.S. cavalry in South Dakota. Signaled the end of thc Plains Indian Wars.

Federal Boarding Schools—Forgiving the Unforgivable

On March 3, 1819, the U.S. Congress passed the Indian Civilization Act *"providing boarding schools and education for Native American children to prevent further decline and final extinction of the Indian tribes, to instruct them in the mode of agriculture suited to their situation, and to help them to read and write."*[7] A $10,000 fund was appropriated for the schools.

Lawmakers believed that by removing Native American children from reservations and reprogramming them, they could destroy tribal community connections and help them assimilate to the white culture. This approach was thought to be less costly than wars against the tribes and elimination of the entire Native American population.

Like so many laws Congress passed to assimilate Native Americans to the Anglo-American culture, the opening of boarding schools had devastating results for many, if not most, tribal children. When attending boarding schools, students as young as two years old were physically and emotionally removed from their family and tribe for a minimum of four and up to twelve years. Many children were separated from their family and tribal influence during the formative years of their lives.[8] According *to* Brave Heart and Debruyn (1998*)*[9] *"the removal of children from their families is considered one of the most devastating traumas that occurred to the Indian people because it resulted in the disruption of the family and community structure and the forced assimilation of children to a white culture that they did not want to become part of."*

According to Dr. Denise Lajimodiere in *Stringing Rosaries*, over the years, there have been 406 federal boarding schools in thirty-one states. There have been eight boarding schools in Nebraska: Genoa Industrial School, Iowa Industrial School, Omaha Indian School, Oto and Missouri Agency Industrial, Santee Industrial, Santee Normal Training School, St. Augustine's School, and the Winnebago School.[10] The Genoa Industrial School in Nebraska was the fourth federal boarding school to be built in the U.S. and operated from 1884 to 1914.

At its peak in 1932, the Genoa School's campus was 640 acres, and the school was home to over 599 Native American students who ranged in age from four to twenty-two years old. Students were brought to Genoa from forty different tribes, and at least eighty-six students are believed to have died at the school. It is believed that most of the students died from infectious diseases. There was one recording of an accidental shooting and drowning. Currently, tribal leaders have organized search teams to find the exact locations of the students' graves on the campus. Students who lived and died at the school should not be forgotten.

In addition, the Genoa U.S. Indian School Foundation purchased a building on the Genoa campus in 1999 from the city of Genoa, and they have worked to restore it. The building is now an Interpretative Center which opened in May 2023. The Center has tribal flags hanging from the ceiling and displays traditional clothing, photos of former students, school records, and artifacts. Educational programs are presented to describe and honor tribal cultures and spirituality

By 1931, thirty percent of Native American children in school were in boarding schools. It is estimated that two-thirds of Native Americans have attended boarding school at some point in their life. Boarding schools were located "on" and "off" reservations. Policy makers did not believe that schools located "on" the reservations were effectively achieving the goal of assimilation to the white culture. They were opposed to Native American children going home from school every day and back to their tribal traditions. Unfortunately, students appeared to suffer the most when they were sent to schools "off" the reservation and when schools were hundreds of miles from their homes. Children were often forced to remain in these schools and never see their parents for multiple years—sometimes for over a decade.

During the years 1879 to 1920, boarding schools were especially damaging to children. In 1879, Captain Richard Pratt, an educator, campaigned the government for off-reservation boarding schools to be placed in unused cavalry barracks; he wanted to develop these schools using a military model. Captain Pratt had been a frontier Indian fighter and served in the Civil War before becoming an educator. He believed that civilization must triumph over savagery. The schools he opened were organized around rigid, strict, and often harsh military standards. These schools used whistles, bells, bugles, military school punishment, and guard houses.[11]

Students were literally stolen from their families to attend these schools. A compulsory attendance law was passed by Congress in 1891. The law authorized the Indian agency to *"withhold rations, clothing, and other annuities from Indian parents or guardians who refused or neglected to send and keep their children in some school a reasonable portion of each year.*"[12] There are stories of children taken from their homes by force and put on trains to arrive at schools that were hundreds, and in one case, thousands of miles from their home. Conductors reported that Native American children on the trains to boarding schools would be crying, screaming, and scared to death, with no one to console them.

Children at the school were slapped or beaten for speaking their tribal language. Their hair was cut, and their only parenting at the school was the strict military style corporal punishment. The "cutting of hair" may not seem to white Americans as such a traumatic event. However, Native Americans believe that "just like a tree has branches that extend to the root of the tree, hair extends to the spirit of the person." When Native Americans lose their hair, they believe they lose a part of who they are." [13]

At many of the schools, there was a total lack of love and caring, and an absolute forbiddance of tribal traditions. Government expenditures for boarding schools were always small, and the schools exploited the free labor of children to be able to function. Due to overcrowding in these schools, TB, trachoma, measles, pneumonia, and influenza swept through the overcrowded dormitories. Diseases and death were frequent aspects of the boarding school experience.

In her book entitled *Stringing Rosaries: The History, the Unforgivable, and the Healing of Northern Plains American Indian Boarding School Survivors*, Dr. Denise Lajimodiere shared the results of a qualitative study she conducted analyzing interviews with survivors of Northern Plains Native American boarding schools. Dr. Lajimodiere was an associate professor and educator at the North Dakota State University, and her father was a member of the Chippewa tribe and a boarding school survivor. She had heard multiple stories of the damaging effects of boarding schools and was determined to share these stories with the public.

Some students who attended boarding schools did report having positive experiences, especially when schools were located on the reservation. Also, some students came from homes that were less than ideal. Students were often raised by grandparents, and they did go to bed hungry some days. At least they experienced love in their home, however, and felt a part of their tribal community. Susan and Francis La Flesche both benefited from their experiences at boarding schools, and especially enjoyed reading the English language literature. Susan and Francis may not have been typical of most Native American children. The La Flesche family, especially their father Joseph La Flesche, was extremely supportive of education. Dr. Lajimodiere's own father worked throughout his life as a carpenter and learned the carpentry trade at a boarding school. Other survivors reported that trades they learned at the schools were not helpful for either Anglo or Native American job positions. Two Native Americans who attended boarding school and were well-known to Nebraskans are Jim Thorpe and Nebraska State Senator Tom Brewer.

Most of the students interviewed by Dr. Lajimodiere reported negative experiences at boarding schools, and some of these experiences were tragic. Survivors told of being hungry at schools, being ridiculed, and suffering emotional and physical abuse. Illnesses were common, and children died at schools. Native Americans interviewed for the study reported that attending boarding schools left them with an "overwhelming feeling of loss."[14] They lost their language, identity, culture, tradition, and self-esteem. They were lonely and felt abandoned by their tribe. They were forced to work as child laborers. Survivors reported "soul trauma." They stated that prior to the interviews they had suffered in silence. They believed that for healing and forgiveness to occur, they needed the U.S. government to offer them an apology,

The present Interior Secretary of the U.S., Deb Haaland, a Native American herself, announced a program she was starting entitled the *Federal Indian Boarding School Truth Initiative*. She embarked on a nationwide listening tour, giving survivors a chance to share accounts of systematic abuse at boarding schools. The following is an example of one Native American student's experience.

A Native American victim in North Dakota, Dr. Ramona Klein, spent four years at a federal boarding school in the 1950s. She later became an educator and mother of two and is now seventy-five years old. However, she still remembers her tragic and traumatic experiences at the school. She says she is sharing her boarding school experience as part of her healing process. The following are excerpts from her story:[15]

> *I was seven when I arrived at the school. One of the first things that happened when we got to the school is they cut my hair. I often had hunger pangs. When I disobeyed, I was hit with a paddle. It was a green board that the teachers called "the board of education." I had bruises from the paddle, but the bruises didn't hurt as much as the "lack of emotional connection." There was no love or caring either from the teachers or from the other students at the school. I cried myself to sleep at night from loneliness. I remember being made to feel very dumb. For healing from boarding school abuses, we need a voice. Without a doubt. We need to be heard.*

Based on Dr. Haaland's work, a massive report on the schools was released in 2022. So far, the investigation identified more than 500 Native American student deaths at nineteen schools. That number is expected to climb to the thousands or even tens of thousands. The department found at least fifty-three burial sites at or near the boarding schools.

In the last decades, multiple healing resources for children and survivors of boarding schools have been made available. One example of a resource is the White Bison Center for Wellbeing founded by Don Coyhis in 1998. White Bison offers sobriety recovery, addiction prevention, and wellness learning resources to Native American communities nationwide. During the summer of 2009, staff at White Bison began a 7000-mile healing journey, called the *Journey of Forgiveness*, across the United States. The journey was to help raise awareness of human rights violations and historical and intergenerational trauma caused by boarding school abuses. They attended twenty-four boarding school sites and heard stories from survivors at each of the sites. The goal was for survivors to receive healing, hope, unity, and power, allowing them to forgive the unforgivable.

Coyhis reported: *"The stories were unbelievable.[16] We now know that what was done to the children in these boarding schools is directly tied to the social issues we are currently experiencing in our communities. We call this intergenerational trauma. The elders told us that they would not be free from this trauma unless we could forgive the unforgivable."*

According to Coyhis, survivors believed that a first step in healing their trauma would be for the U.S. government and all Americans to recognize and admit to mistreatment of Native Americans in the past. In addition, for Native Americans to heal they should not be considered isolated, or dispossessed, victims. Rather, they should be incorporated into our society as *knowledgeable, empowered, and belonging equals.*

Addiction to Alcohol in Indians as a Response to Generations of Historical Trauma

During her time practicing on the reservation, one priority for Susan La Flesche was to fight against the problem of alcohol abuse among her people. One compelling cause for this problem among Native Americans is historical trauma. Patients who are addicted admit that they often use alcohol to numb the pain of anxiety, depression, and trauma—including historical trauma.

Alcohol was introduced to the Omaha tribe in the 1700s by the Anglo American or white settlers, Army personnel, and fur traders. By the 1800s, alcohol addiction among tribal members was disrupting family and community structure. In the 1850s, Susan's father and chief of the Omaha tribe, Joseph La Flesche, declared it illegal to drink alcohol on the Macy Reservation. For more than three decades, until Joseph's death in 1888, alcohol abuse reduced drastically. During these years, the Native Americans on the reservation made tremendous progress in building their community. They built wooden homes, tended to farms, sent children to school, and lived in secure, extended families.

In addition to Joseph La Flesche's declaration, in 1896, a Nebraska senator Named George Meiklejohn sponsored a bill to prohibit the sale of intoxicating liquors to Native Americans. The "Meiklejohn Bill" passed in January 1897, making it a crime for anyone to sell or supply liquor to any Native American supervised by the government. Convictions would result in imprisonment and fines. Unfortunately, in 1899, the Justice Department removed its local deputy marshal and alcohol consumption resumed.

In 1899 and in the years after, liquor or "demon rum" changed the Macy Reservation. Farms were neglected, and tribal members who abused alcohol became easy prey to TB. Alcohol addiction resulted in poor physical and mental health as well as behavioral issues.

What Is Alcohol Addiction? Alcoholism, or alcohol addiction, has been described as *a chemical process in the brain that changes the way the brain reacts to alcohol.* It impairs the person's decision-making abilities, at least when it comes to using this substance. As a result, alcoholics lose the ability to make rational judgments as to when to start and stop drinking alcohol. "*We know that while alcoholics may be able to avoid using substances for considerable periods or in situations where it's necessary, they usually have enormous difficulty regulating or moderating their alcohol consumption once they do start using.*"[17] While alcoholics may be strong-willed and courageous people in most situations, their strong will is often not enough to control their alcohol intake.

Addiction to alcohol can have extremely negative consequences. Alcoholics can lose their jobs and the support of their friends and family. They can conduct unlawful activities. Alcoholism can contribute to numerous health problems—including heart disease, liver disease, diabetes, and TB.

Although treatments are available for alcoholism, a patient is never considered cured of this addiction. At best, it can be managed as a lifelong chronic condition, much like diabetes. But the fact that it can be managed, and often is, is still an enormous advancement. Based on literature, for the time being, the only totally safe solution for addiction to alcohol is complete abstinence. Managing addiction to alcohol doesn't just mean abstinence. It also means finding a new way of coping with all of life's challenges.

What Causes This Addiction? There is no single explanation for why some people become addicted to alcohol. The reasons that someone becomes addicted are unique to each person, and the path to recovery is also unique.

According to research, some people are born with a greater genetic or biological susceptibility to addiction.[18] Next, stressful situations or traumatic experiences may trigger this susceptibility.[19] Some researchers have concluded that, in many cases, addiction is approximately 50 percent related to genetics and 50 percent related to stress and the environment.

Although there appears to be no one single alcohol gene, studies have identified multiple genes that directly or indirectly increase a person's risk for alcoholism and addictions. Since 1989, the NIAAA (National Institute for Alcohol Addiction and Abuse) funded a Collaborative on Genetics of Alcoholism (COGA). Goals of the study are to develop more effective ways to prevent and treat alcoholism by identifying the specific genes and altering the expression of these genes.

Treatments for Alcohol Addiction Today. One of the first successful treatment programs for alcohol addiction for all Americans was the Alcoholic Anonymous (AA) twelve-step program. Bill Wilson and Bob Smith in Akron, Ohio, founded the AA program in 1935. One of the premises of the twelve-step program is that the key to recovery is to turn your life over to a "higher power." This is consistent with Susan La Flesche's encouraging her patients to have faith in a Greater Spirit.

Effective programs today often combine therapy and counseling with medications. Medications prescribed could include (a) *Naltrexone* to reduce cravings; (b) *disulfiram* or *Antabuse,* which causes people to become nauseated after drinking alcohol; and (c) *acamprosate,* which reduces symptoms that cause people to drink, such as anxiety and inability to sleep.[20]

Not all alcohol addicts have the same genetic background or the same experiences in life. No single treatment approach works for everyone with alcohol addiction. For some patients, no treatment appears to work. Tragically, however, many people in the U.S. with alcohol addiction never receive treatment.

Susan La Flesche's Fight against Alcohol Abuse

Susan fought desperately to prevent the spread of alcoholism in the late 1800s when alcohol was no longer banned from the reservation. Before

1888, she believed that the Omaha people were both moral and in good physical and mental health. In 1888, after alcohol was allowed on the reservation, she wrote of observing more violence, vandalism, and breakdowns in family structure. In 1892, she advocated for tough new laws against alcohol abuse that would restore order to the reservation. She made multiple trips to the state legislature and impassioned speeches against the whiskey peddlers preying on the Omaha tribe. In 1907, she requested that liquor sales be prohibited in any town along the Macy reservation borders.[21] She advocated for the banning of alcohol in her letters, presentations, and church sermons. In 1905, after ten years of marriage, Susan's own husband, Henry Picotte, died from a combination of TB and alcoholism. Henry's death was especially discouraging because Susan had fought so long and so hard against alcoholism.

Susan La Flesche's Fight to Prevent Historical Trauma

One cause of alcohol abuse among Native Americans was the stress they experienced when attempting to survive in the white dominant culture. Susan understood that to interact with the white culture, the Omaha people had a very steep hill to climb. They had to adjust to a different language, a different lifestyle and culture, and different ways of providing for their family. They felt a sense of grief for all the lands they had lost and their many ancestors who had died due to infectious diseases. When Susan began her practice in the 1890s, she wrote about the anxiety, depression, hopelessness, and sense of loss she observed in her patients. Even today, compared to other races, Native Americans are more likely to be diagnosed with depression.[22] In her medical practice, she encouraged her tribal patients to continue with the use of herbal therapy and traditional methods of healing such as sweat lodges. Susan only objected to practices that she believed were detrimental to their health. To help her patients interact with white culture, she encouraged them to learn to speak English. She stressed the importance of education, and she and her sister Marguerite started a library on the reservation.

Susan believed that many of the depression and mental health problems she observed on the reservation were due to the Native American's lack of self-confidence and feelings of inadequacy in dealing with the increasing complexity of everyday living. In 1889, she wrote: "*If one wants to make a difference, they must go out every day. These Omaha need help in many aspects of life . . . business, land, money, and horses, what kind to buy and all.*"[23]

Susan had heated discussions with state legislators on land issues and on expanding the legal rights of Native American women and children. She translated legal documents and helped tribal members to understand the technicalities of property deeds. Unfortunately, the government had done little to encourage Native Americans to develop business skills. The Omaha people had not learned how to handle money or to navigate legal red tape. They had no protection from whiskey peddlers or unscrupulous land swindlers.

Susan established clubs and a reading room for people on the reservation with newspapers and games. She helped with a night school and supported various community projects, lectures, and concerts. When an elderly Omaha man could not read a letter the government had sent him, he asked Susan for help. Susan was available when an Omaha tribal member could not understand the technicalities of a property deed, or when someone needed a letter written to the reservation agent. She was a member of a new chapter of the Order of the Eastern Star, was chair of the Nebraska Federation of Women's Clubs, and was president of the missionary society. She taught Sunday school. She entertained tribal leaders and legislators in her home. When the Omaha tribe had disputes against the U.S. government or Anglo Americans, they always asked Susan to be their spokesperson. She wrote numerous letters to lawmakers and congressmen about the continuing concerns of the Omaha people. To help with all the letters she was writing, she eventually exchanged her pen for a typewriter. When Joseph La Flesche died, the Omaha people needed a leader to help them survive the difficult years ahead. Susan La Flesche became that leader. After her death, Susan was honored as a "*virtual chief without having a title. Her word was higher law in the tribe than that of the Indian agent.*"[24]

On one occasion, Susan took a train to Washington, D.C to crusade against the federal policies that resulted in the stealing of land from her people. White settlers were anxious to purchase land from the Omaha people. Too often, the Omaha people sold their land at low prices, and then became destitute after they squandered all the money from the sale.

Susan believed in the Native American philosophy of health. She believed that coping with stress meant helping patients return to a balance of body, mind, and spirit. To cleanse the body and mind, she advocated a healthy diet, exercise, relaxation, and fresh air. In addition, she strongly believed in the spiritual aspect of healing, and advocated faith, meditation, forgiveness, and prayer. She encouraged faith in a Greater Spirit. She understood that for Omaha people, the Great Spirit could be named Wakonda or could also be named Jesus Christ.

Current Treatments for Health and Behavioral Problems Related to Historical Trauma

When caring for Native American patients, physicians today should understand that historical losses and trauma have a role in causing their patient's physical and mental health problems. Historical trauma can impact every part of their patient's life, including their personal identity, interpersonal relationships, and their health. Treatment for historical trauma includes respect for the Native American language, traditions, culture, and spiritual beliefs. Programs are more effective when they incorporate traditional healing approaches used by Native Americans, including sweat lodges, music, and prayers. Specific counseling and therapy, especially mental health programs, should be targeted to needs of individual patients. In addition, cultural and spiritual tribal leaders and family members should be included in treatment programs. The strength of Native Americans suffering from trauma should be reaffirmed as well as their place within the community.

All communities should be involved in preventing and healing historical trauma. In 2009, the U.S. Congress passed Senate Joint Resolution 14, acknowledging a long history of official degradations and ill-conceived policies by the Federal Government regarding Native Americans.[25] This acknowledgment is a first step in promoting survivor healing. Native Americans were the first inhabitants of the state of Nebraska. They deserve our thanks, respect, and protection.

Susan La Flesche: The Last Days of a Remarkable Leader

In 1915, Susan was terribly ill with cancer, and the cancer took her life. From early childhood, Susan's goal was not only to become a doctor, but also to be an advocate for Native American rights. Thus, although she was in poor health, her Omaha tribe convinced her to make one last trip to see the Secretary of the Interior Department and the Attorney General of the United States. Once again, she battled for the rights of the Omaha people.

Susan had always been frail and prone to illness. She became even more frail in 1906 after her husband Henry died, and she had moved back to Walthill, Nebraska. Susan was bedfast for months at a time. She had migraine headaches, fatigue, depression, and poor digestion. At the end of her life, Susan was diagnosed with what was believed to be facial bone cancer, and she died at the age of fifty. She is buried with her husband Henry and near her family members in Bancroft, Nebraska.[26]

Susan La Flesche Picotte grave in Bancroft. Nebraska.
Nebraska State Historical Society Photograph Collections.

Although Susan died at the early age of fifty, she accomplished a great deal during her lifetime. The following is a tribute given in the local paper at the time of her death. The writer was Harry Keefe, a friend of Susan's, an attorney at Walthill and president of the Nebraska Farm Bureau.[27]

> *We are confronted here with a character rising to greatness, and to great deeds out of conditions which seldom produce more than mediocre men and women, achieving great and beneficial ends over obstacles almost insurmountable. In her death the Indians lose their best and truest friend; the community and state sustains an irreparable loss; and there is ended one of the most fruitful, unselfish, and useful lives.*

Although Susan La Flesche was of mixed blood, she described herself as a Native American. In her early years, she was exposed to the luxury and glamour of the big cities of White America. Yet, she established her medical practice at the Macy reservation. Her best friends and family were from her tribe, and she married a Native American, Henry Picotte. Susan was respected in the larger American society, but she never lost her Native American ways. Susan's belief in the value of "education, service, stewardship, and justice" still inspires Americans today.[28]

After her death, the name of the Walthill hospital was changed to the Dr. Susan La Flesche Picotte Memorial Hospital by the Home Mission Board. In 1947, the hospital closed, and in 1988, the hospital building became the Dr. Susan La Flesche Picotte Center. In 1989, the building became a historical landmark on the registry of historic places.

At the celebration of the historic landmark, Congressman Doug Bereuter of Nebraska gave the following tribute in the U.S. House of Representatives to Susan La Flesche's life. Representative Bereuter stated that Susan's "*own accomplishments were the means to bridge the cultural and economic gulf that threatens to divide the Indian people and non-Indians. . . . Her public accomplishments are a reminder that color and culture are no barriers to success and respect.*"[29]

There have been numerous tributes to Dr. Susan La Flesche. In 1993, an elementary school in the city of Omaha was named for Susan. A statue of Susan was dedicated at the east side of the Centennial Mall in Lincoln, Nebraska, on October 10, 2021.

At the end of her life, Susan was quoted as saying: "*I have lived right with them for over twenty years practicing medicine, attending the sick, helping them with all their financial and domestic business and anything that concerned their personal family life. and I cannot see how any credit is due me. I am only thankful that I have been called and permitted to serve. I feel blessed for the privilege.'*[30]

TEN

The Omaha People Today

Susan's sons, Caryl and Pierre, were both successful in life although neither son chose a career in medicine. Both sons attended Bellevue College and the Nebraska Military Academy in Lincoln. When the U.S. entered World War I, they enlisted to join the war effort.

Caryl served in the Army for twenty-eight years and attained the rank of Lieutenant Colonel. During World War II, he was sent to the Philippines and survived the Bataan Death March. He was a prisoner of war for three or four years, and for his services, he was recommended for the Distinguished Service Cross and received the Bronze Star. After retirement from the military, he and his wife and son Caryl Jr. bought a horse ranch and lived in San Diego, California. Caryl died in 1978 at the age of eighty-three.

After service in the military, Pierre returned to Walthill, Nebraska, married, and had three children. He listed his profession as "farming." Later, his family moved to Los Angeles California, and he was believed to work in the automobile industry. Pierre died in 1982 at the age of eighty-four. Caryl was buried in San Diego, and Pierre, in Los Angeles, California.[1]

The original hospital in Walthill that Susan had helped to build is now the Dr. Susan La Flesche Picotte Center. The Center is in the process of restoration, and the restored Center will be a great asset to the Omaha tribe, the citizens of Walthill, and the people of Nebraska.[2]

The People of the Omaha Tribe are Surviving!

Photo of Pierre Picotte at age 81
Courtesy of Susan Picotte, great-granddaughter of Pierre Picotte.

Currently, the Omaha Nation is no longer governed by a chief. Instead, a tribal council is elected by the Omaha people every three years, and the council has authority over decisions related to the tribe.

The Macy (Omaha) reservation is located in Thurston county, north of Omaha and bordering the Missouri River. In the 2020 federal census, 5,247 Americans were listed as Native Americans from the Omaha tribe.[3] The population on the reservation was 4,526, and only 47.6 percent of the population (or approximately 2150 people) were Omaha tribal members. Thus, more than 50 percent of the Omaha tribe make their homes outside the reservation. Many of the Omaha people live in surrounding urban centers such as Omaha and Lincoln, Nebraska, and Sioux City, Iowa. Most likely, the Omaha tribal members moved from the reservation for more options in employment. The income per person in Thurston county is lower than in other Nebraska counties. In 2020, the median household income for Native Americans in Nebraska was only $25,700.[4]

When the Macy reservation first opened, the Omaha people believed they owned 300,000 acres of land. Currently, the Omaha tribe own a great deal less than this. After the initial treaty with the Omaha tribe, the U.S. government gave a northern portion of the land on the Macy reservation to the Winnebago tribe. The Omaha tribe lost more land because of the Dawes Act, when many tribal members who were allotted land sold their land to the white settlers. The land sold to white settlers is now mostly used for farming. Currently, Omaha people on the reservation generally work at local businesses, in the tribal offices, at the schools, at the health education center, on the farms, and at the casino.

Towns on the reservation include Macy, Walthill, Rosalie, and Pender. The northernmost part of Bancroft is also within reservation boundaries. Of the five towns, Macy and Walthill have the largest population of

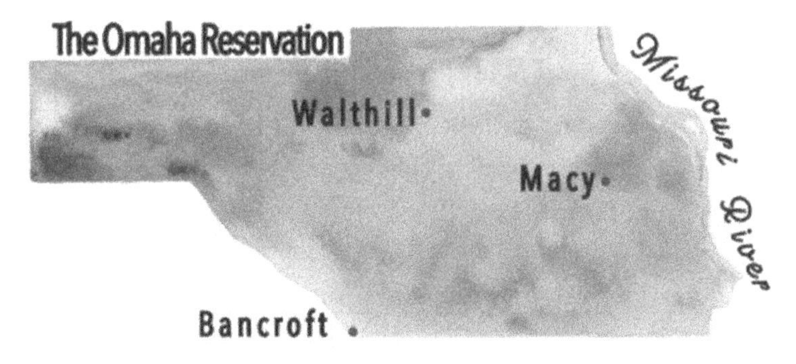

Macy Reservation
Towns of Walthill, and Macy; Bancroft is at southern edge of reservation. Illustration by Erica Parker Rogers.

Omaha people. The town of Macy is the tribal seat for the reservation. As of 2020, the population of Macy was 1,045 with 229 households, and 98.5 percent of Macy's population were Native Americans. In addition to other businesses, the town of Macy has a tribal college offering a two-year degree program, a public school with a career academy and culture program, pow wow grounds, a skate park, tribal offices, and the Carl T. Curtis Health Education center.

Susan La Flesche's House in Walthill
Along with restoration of the Dr. Susan La Flesche Picotte Center, plans are underway to restore Susan's house in Walthill. She lived in the house with her children from 1905 to 1915. Photo by Nancy Waltman

In 2020, the population of Walthill was 780 with 207 households, and 80.9 percent of the residents were Native Americans. Walthill has a library, gift shop, coffee shop, casino, skate park, and public school. Dr. Susan's house and the Dr. Susan La Flesche Picotte Center are in Walthill.

The Omaha People continue to practice traditions of their tribe.[5] Powwows are held at least annually and last several days. At powwows, Omaha people gather for singing, dancing, and socialization and there is a sense of community and belonging. Various families on the reservation run sweat lodges on a regular basis. Lodges are often used for healing, for mourning rituals, and to celebrate a birthday or new baby.

When there are deaths on the reservation, wakes and funerals are conducted today much the same as they were conducted hundreds of years ago. A four-day wake is held prior to the deceased person's funeral. During these four days, the body is on display, and a member of the family is always present to honor the body. Family members are not allowed to weep during the wake, because this will make the deceased person sad as he ascends into heaven. After the four days, a funeral is held, and most members in the community attend to honor the deceased person.

The Sacred Pole or "Venerable Man," a valuable artifact of the Omaha tribe, is at Lincoln, Nebraska, in the vaults of the History Nebraska museum. The Pole (or man) remains under security and can only be removed when the tribal council requests his presence at an event. More information on the Sacred Pole is included in chapter one.

The Health Statistics for Nebraska Native Americans, Including the Omaha Tribe

There are recent (2020) health statistics for Nebraska Native Americans in general; statistics are not specific for the Omaha people. As with other Nebraskans, most Nebraska Native Americans die of cancer and heart disease.[6] Infectious diseases are no longer leading causes of death. Compared to other Americans, Native Americans in Nebraska are more likely to die from unintentional injuries (such as motor vehicle accidents, alcohol-related deaths, and poisonings), from liver disease, and from diabetes.[7] Native Americans continue to have more physical and mental health problems.[8]

Positive findings from the statistics report are that flu and pneumonia vaccination rates are higher for Native Americans than for other Nebraskans.[9] Also, in the last two decades, diabetes mortality rates have decreased from 93.2 to 67.9 per 100,000, and alcohol induced mortality rates have decreased from 86.1 to 54.6 per 100,000 people.

More assistance with health care needs is now available. At Macy and Walthill, residents have access to numerous health care facilities. Programs are available to meet patient needs related to behavioral and substance abuse problems and to manage patients with diabetes or other chronic illnesses. There is a family medicine clinic, dental clinic, dialysis unit, and a pharmacy.

The Omaha people can obtain many health care services such as vaccinations and screenings at free or reduced costs through the Indian Health Service (IHS). Unfortunately, during times of budget cuts, federal funding for the IHS is often reduced. At present, it is estimated that IHS funding is only enough to meet 60% of the health care needs for eligible Native Americans. As a result, IHS expenditures are prioritized based on patient needs. To pay for health care expenses not covered by IHS, Omaha people often sign up for insurance through the Affordable Care Act or they seek employers who offer health insurance programs.

Federally recognized tribes on reservations do have the right to govern themselves, their lands, and their people.

The U.S, Bureau of Indian Affairs can provide general assistance as needed for food, clothing, shelter, and utilities. Generally, no Nebraska tax is imposed on a Native American living on a reservation located within the state of Nebraska. If Omaha people have a Nebraska State Tax Exemption Identification card, they do not pay state property taxes for land they own on the reservation. They are exempt from state motor vehicle taxes for vehicles registered on the reservation. They are exempt from state income taxes for work on the reservation.

The Native American Rights Fund. The benefits people on the reservation receive are because of treaties previously signed with the U.S.

Government. There are still barriers to economic growth of Native people, however, due to the arduous bureaucratic processes reservation people encounter when working with our government. There is an organization, the Native American Rights Fund, or NARF, that works to protect the interests of tribal people. The stated purpose of NARF is to preserve and protect the rights of all Native People, taking the battles to the courts if necessary.

The Proud History of the Omaha People[10]

The Omaha tribe has had great leaders such as Chiefs Blackbird, Big Elk, Logan Fontanelle, and Joseph La Flesche. Tribal members such as Susette, Francis, and Susan La Flesche have been acclaimed nationally as prominent leaders in their fields. Throughout history, the Omaha people have been good stewards of the land. They have shared their bounties with others in their tribe and have been loyal to their country—the United States of America. Native Americans have consistently volunteered to defend the U.S. in foreign wars. Since the beginning of the 1900s, over 19 percent of eligible Native Americans have served in the U.S. military compared to an average of 14 percent for all other racial groups. The proud history of Native Americans and the Omaha tribe should be celebrated by all Nebraskans.

Attitudes of Americans and policies of the U.S. government are changing. In the past, Native Americans have been the target of racist and prejudicial beliefs and of physical and emotional abuse by our government and by the white dominant society. The truth about abuse of Native American children at federal boarding schools has finally been exposed in a massive report. This is due to the work of the U.S. Secretary of the Interior, Deb Haaland, and her Federal Indian Boarding School Truth Initiative.

The causes of societal problems in Native Americans and in all Americans are complex. There is no one cause for societal problems and there is no one solution. In this book, the author proposes that historical losses and traumas are a probable cause for some of the mental, physical, and behavioral problems in Omaha tribal members today. According to the renowned Omaha tribal member and historian Dennis Hastings: "*We cannot correctly understand the present if we have a distorted interpretation of the past. Knowledge about, and correction of past injustices occurring in our nation is not simply a service to those who have been wronged, it is a service to everyone.*"[11]

In recent times, the U.S. government as well as Anglo American people have recognized that they have been a part of the abuse of Native Americans, and they have tried to make amends. The following paragraphs are examples of U.S. government policies and other American activities that assist in the healing of past trauma. "*Honoring and empowering American Indians provides them with a sense of identity and belonging—a means of overcoming a collective inferiority complex.*"[12]

Honoring Native Americans—The First Inhabitants of Nebraska and Our Nation

In some states and cities in the U.S., the second Monday in October is honored as Indigenous People's Day. Every November has been designated as Native American Heritage month. Native Americans such as Susan La Flesche, Susette and Francis La Flesche, Joseph La Flesche, Big Elk, Logan Fontanelle, and Standing Bear have been honored in numerous ways; their honors have been described previously.

Preserving Native American Language, Culture, and Traditions

Since the time of Big Elk, the Omaha people have wanted to interact with the Anglo Americans. They have wanted to succeed in a white dominant society and to be respected by this society. They have also desired to honor their past—their parents and grandparents and their ancestors throughout history. Susan La Flesche was quoted as saying, "*The old ways are not devoid of values, culture, and emotional ties. They need to always be preserved.*"[13]

The American Civil Liberties Union (ACLU) recently "*affirmed their support for the rights of all Native American people to retain their culture and religious tradition and practices.*"[14] By practicing their culture and traditions, Omaha people are showing pride in the history of their tribe. They are honoring the wisdom of their ancestors. Even in a white dominant society, they are maintaining their identity. The following are recent examples of how Nebraskans and all Americans have helped Native Americans to retain their culture and traditions.

Publishing Tribal Customs and Traditions

An Omaha tribal member, Dr. Dennis Hastings, spent decades meticulously researching and documenting five centuries of Omaha tribal history. His twenty books of writings are entitled *Four Hills of Life: Umonhon Curriculum*. The twenty books include Omaha cookbooks, traditional tales and songs, a workbook of the Omaha language, and numerous works of art. Unfortunately, Dr. Hastings died In May of 2022, at the age seventy-four, before his books could be published. Currently, two Anglo Americans, Richard Chilton and Margery Coffee, are working on behalf of the Omaha Tribal Historical Research Project to carry on Hasting's legacy and to publish the books. According to Coffee, this is a way of giving back to the Omaha people. "*They need to know their history, and they don't. It's been taken away from them. Omaha people need to be what they are and not what the white man insists that they be. We want the Omaha people to be proud of their present and proud of their future.*"[15] A fundraising drive has been initiated to pay the costs of publishing the books.

The Adopt-A-Buffalo Program[16]

The Native Americans have always had a cultural and spiritual connection with the buffalo, and they have grieved for their loss. The loss of the buffalo was described by Crow Chief Plenty Coups as the following: "*When the buffalo went away, the hearts of my people fell to the ground, and they could not lift them up again. After this, nothing happened. There was little singing anywhere.*"[17]

The Intertribal Bison Council (IBC) at the Federal Bureau of Indian Affairs believes that the buffalo would help to heal the spirit of Native American people and protect the traditional relationships between the people and the buffalo. In 2010, the Federal Bureau of Indian Affairs approved an IBC proposal aimed at increasing the number of buffalo herds in midwestern and western Native American reservations. The Ponca tribe in northeast Nebraska now have a herd of nearly 100 buffalo in two different pastures. The tribe also participates in an Adopt-A Buffalo program to increase the size of their herds. Recently, the principal and staff at Standing Bear High School in Lincoln, Nebraska, wanted to honor Standing Bear, a Ponca tribal member, by adopting a buffalo. They applied to the program and have received a letter certifying that the high school has now adopted a buffalo living on the reservation. They also received a picture of the buffalo they adopted and have posted the picture in the school.

A Kindergarten through High School Cultural Learning Program

More than 150 years ago, federal policies and administrators prescribed that boarding schools should no longer be using the Native American languages in their schools and should no longer allow students to practice their traditions. Thus, even today, teachers are not using native languages or traditions in any of the public schools. This may be one reason why high school graduation rates for Native Americans in Nebraska have been low. In 2020, only 69 percent of Native Americans in Nebraska had obtained a high school degree; 3.2 percent who were enrolled in high school withdrew before completion.[18]

At the Santee Dakota Sioux Indian school near Niobrara, Nebraska, elementary through high school students are being taught Dakota Sioux history, language, and customs as part of a new cultural learning program. In addition, the Sioux language and culture are incorporated in their school lessons. Since the beginning of the program, administered by the director Redwing Thomas, the attendance rate at the school has increased and is now at over 88 percent. The school has had 100 percent graduation rate two years running. Teachers and parents say the cultural program has increased student enthusiasm and performance in all areas of education. Students call themselves "Ozuyapi" or warriors. According to Director Thomas, students understand that their tribe has experienced "generational trauma." This is not a story of sorrow or sadness, but one of strength. Thomas believes the tribe has survived so much. "*The story at the Santee school is a story of how the Santee Sioux students can persevere.*"[19]

Incorporating Native Americans into U.S. Society as Knowledgeable, Empowered, and Belonging Equals

Providing More Educational Opportunities. In December 2022, the University of Nebraska Medical Center Department of Public Health announced the first *Dr. Susan and Suzette La Flesche Public Health Scholarship* recipient. She is Kirsten Concho-Moore, a physician and member of the Taos Pueblo tribe, and she will enroll in courses leading to a PhD in Public Health beginning the spring of 2023. This scholarship is to support Public Health students interested in improving the lives of Native Americans. Dr. Susan La Flesche advocated for public health more than a century ago.

Including Native Americans in Decision Making

Americans are electing more indigenous people to local, state, and federal offices. Historically, Native Americans have been excluded from discussions and decisions on government policies. Today, more Native Americans than ever before are holding offices at all levels of government. In 1918, there were at least fifty-eight Native Americans elected to local and state offices nationwide, and some of these Native Americans were elected in Nebraska.

In 2022, a record number of Native people were elected to the 118th Congress. Ideally, even more Native Americans should be holding federal offices and representing their people. In the senate, only one of 100 members (1 percent), and in Congress, only four of 435 members (0.9%) are Native Americans.

In November of this year, 2022, President Joe Biden recognized the need for more Native Americans to be involved in government and pledged to give them a stronger voice in federal affairs. He promised an in-person summit[20] as one method for consulting with tribes. Tribes are to be included in decision-making and funding for communities—especially in relation to struggles with climate change.

We Are Still Here. We Shall Remain.

Despite facing numerous obstacles, the Omaha people are surviving, and all Americans are thankful for this. Nebraskans, both Native and Non-Native, are working for "fair and balanced" laws for all people in our state. We believe that U.S. commitments in treaties should continue to be honored for all Native Americans, including the Omaha tribe. The Omaha or "*upstream*" tribal people have been fighting the currents for centuries. Today, the Omaha are blessed with good leaders and with Nebraskans who are helping them to succeed. The Omaha people will succeed. They are here to stay.

End Notes

Throughout End Notes, "direct quotations" are written in italics.

Introduction

1. *"My blood is the same color as your blood."* A quote by Standing Bear in Starita, Joe. (2008). *"I am a Man": Chief Standing Bear's Journey for Justice,* 151.

2. "*Healing the body must first begin with healing the spirit. The body cannot be healed until the mind and spirit are also healed."* Cichoke, Anthony J. (2001) *Secrets of Native American Herbal Remedies*, 203.

3. "Dispossession." Wishart, David. (1994). *Unspeakable Sadness; The Dispossession of the Nebraska Indians,* xiii–xiv.

4. *"Omaha Indians continue to negotiate their lives." Wishart, David (2007). Encyclopedia of the Great Plains Indians, 140.*

Chapter One—The History and Culture of the Omaha People

For readers wanting a comprehensive history of the Omaha tribe, I recommend: La Flesche, F. & Fletcher, A. (1972) *The Omaha Tribe.* (2 vols.).

This Story will Begin with the (Umaha) Omaha Tribe Migrating West to the Nebraska Territory

1. "The Omaha tribe originally resided." Tong, Benson. (1999*). Susan La Flesche Picotte, MD: Omaha Indian Leader and Reformer,* 138.

2. *"When the snow drifts into the tents."* Starita, Joe. (2016). *A Warrior of the People,* 1.

3. "The Omaha people called themselves." Ibid., 2.

4. "In the 1700s." Boughter, Judith. (1998). *Betraying the Omaha Nation: 1790–1916,* 9.

5. "The introduction of horses." Wishart, David (2007). *Encyclopedia of the Great Plains Indians,* 83–84.

6. "They first developed friendly relations." La Flesche, F. & Fletcher, A. (1972). The Omaha Tribe. vol. 2, 611.

7. "The Spanish had built a fort". Ibid.

8. "Earth lodges." La Flesche, F. & Fletcher, A. (1972). *The Omaha Tribe.* vol. 1, 97–98.

9. Tipis. Ibid., 95–97.

10. "Life was not easy." Starita, Joe. (2016.) *A Warrior of the People,* 4.

11. "The men provided for and protected their family." La Flesche, F. & Fletcher, A. (1972). *The Omaha Tribe.* vol. 2, 338.

12. "Women cared for the children." Starita, Joe. (2016). *A Warrior of the People,* 4.

13. "Women were well-respected." Ibid., 4.

14. "Young girls were never left unprotected." Ibid., 5.

15. "Loved their children." La Flesche, F. & Fletcher, A. (1972). *The Omaha Tribe.* vol. 2, 327.

16. *"Children were considered the most precious possessions."* Greene, Norma. (1969). *Iron Eye's Family: The Children of Joseph La Flesche.*

17. "Women and children sowed corn." Ferris, Jeri. (1991.) *Native American Doctor: The Story of Susan La Flesche Picotte,* 17.

The Livelihood of Omaha People depended on the Buffalo.

18. "Women used the squash" Ibid., 1.

19. "Two meals a day." La Flesche, F. & Fletcher, A. (1972). *The Omaha Tribe.* vol. 2, 335.

20. "A typical meal." Mullins, G. (2019). *Native American Cooking: An Indian Cookbook with Legends and Folklore* (2nd ed), 146–164.

21. "Fry bread." Ibid., 88–99

George Catlin—An Artist that Preserved the Nebraska Scenery and the Lives of Native Americans and the Omaha Tribe

22. "George Catlin." Hassrick, Royal. (1997). *The George Catlin Book of American Indians,* 15–31.

The Native American Philosophy of Health

23. "The Native American Philosophy of Health." Cichoke, Anthony. (2001) *Secrets of American Herbal Remedies,* 199–204.

24. "Herbs are defined as." Ibid., 2.

25. "Corn silk." Ibid., 38.

26. "Dandelion." Simmons, M. & Irving, J. (2016). *The Gardener's Companion to Medicinal Plants,* 193.

27. "Goldenrod." Ibid., 183.

28. "Pleurisy." Cichoke, Anthony. (2001). *Secrets of American Herbal Remedies,* 65.

29. "Raspberry." Ibid., 66–67.

30. "Strawberry." Simmons, M. & Irving, J. (2016). *The Gardener's Companion To Medicinal Plants.* 86.

31. "Sunflower." Ibid., 101.

32. "Sweet flag." Ibid., 14.

33. Sweet grass." Ibid.

34. "Wild Plum." Cichoke, Anthony. (2001). *Secrets of American Herbal Remedies,*79.

35. "Willow Bark." Ibid., 77–78.

36. "Yarrow," Simmons, M. & Irving, J. (2016). *The Gardener's Companion to Medicinal Plants.* 12–13.

37. "Many of the prescribed drugs." Ibid., 205.

38. "Used for medicinal use." Ibid., 7.

39. "Mind and spirit in balance." Cichoke, Anthony. (2001). *Secrets of American Herbal Remedies,* 205.

40. "Sweat Lodges." Wishart, David. (200*7). Encyclopedia of the Great Plains Indians,* 199–200.

41. "Sacred Pole." Ridington, Robin & Hastings, Dennis. (1997). *Blessing for a Long Time: The Sacred Pole of the Omaha Tri*be, 68–105.

42. *"Generations of white colonizers and their descendants have predicted that Native Americans were a 'vanishing race.'"* Ridington, Robin & Hastings, Dennis. (1997). *Blessing for a Long Time: The Sacred Pole of the Omaha Tribe, p.xx.*

Quackery and Drug Addiction among the Omaha tribe

Peyote: A Hallucinogenic Drug

43. "One drug used by the Omaha People." Tong, Benson. (1999). *Susan La Flesche Picotte, MD: Omaha Indian Leader and Reformer,* 129–131.

44. "M*escal bean is a great evil.*" A quote by Susan La Flesche in. Starita, Joe. (2016). *A Warrior of the People,* 231.

45. "The 1994 amendment to the American Religious Freedom Act." *(1994, October 5). American Religious Freedom Act. Public Law 103–344.*

In the 1800s, the Omaha Indians Faced Numerous Challenges

Chapter Two—Economic and Cultural Dispossession

The Gradual Economic and Cultural Dispossession of the Omaha Tribe

Two books helpful in further understanding the economic and cultural dispossession of the Omaha tribe are: Wishart, David. (1994).

An Unspeakable Sadness: The Dispossession of the Nebraska Indians; and Boughter, Judith A. (1998*). Betraying the Omaha Nation: 1790–1916.*

David Wishart's *Encyclopedia of the Great Plains (2007)* was also extremely useful for writing chapter two. The book features important information on all the Plains Indians and more in-depth examination of words such as "assimilation" and "allotment."

The Louisiana Purchase

1. "The size of the United States doubled**."** *Louisiana Purchase. (2022). https://www.britannica.com/event /Louisiana purchase.*

The Lewis and Clark Expedition

2. "*The white people speak of the country . . . as a wilderness."* A quote by Francis La Flesche). Starita, Joe. (2016). *A Warrior of the People,* 8.

3. "Populated by educated citizen farmers." Ibid., 8.

The U.S. Treaty of 1854—Confinement to a Reservation

4. "Treaty of 1854." Kappler, Charles, ed. (1904***).*** *Indian Affairs: Laws and Treaties*, vol. 2.

5. *"Was determined to lead his people into the future."* Boughter, Judith A. (1998). *Betraying the Omaha Nation: 1790–1916,* 23.

6. 'Flood of whites. *"* A quote by Big Elk. Ibid., 33.

Logan Fontanelle

7. "Murdered and scalped by the Sioux." Starita, Joe. (2016). *A Warrior of the People,* 35–36.

8. "This regulation on the use of alcohol persisted." Tong, Benson. (1999). *Susan La Flesche Picotte, MD: Omaha Indian Leader and Reformer,* 19.

9. *"Politics, greed, and corruption combined to create controversy during the Omahas' early reservation period."* Boughter, Judith A. (1998). *Betraying the Omaha Nation: 1790–1916, 6*

The Homestead Act of 1862

Completion of the Transcontinental Railroad—1868

Demise of the Buffalo

10. "The railroad was also a major cause of the decimation of the buffalo." Davis, Theodore R. (1867, December 14). Buffalo Hunting: Shooting Buffalo from the Trains of the Kansas Pacific Railroad. *Harper's Weekly*.

11. "Buffalo hunts came to an end in the 1870s and 1880s." Wishart, David. (2007). *Encyclopedia of the Great Plains Indians,* 88–89.

The Plains Wars of the post-Civil War Era

12. "Comanches." Ibid., 49–51.

13. "Apaches." Ibid., 21–22.

14. "Cheyenne." Ibid., 47–49.

15. "Kiowa." Ibid., 106–107.

16. "Sioux." Ibid., 184–188.

Warren Wagon Train Raid

17. "Warren Wagon Train Raid." Hamilton, Allen. (1986). *The Warren Wagon Train Raid: Frontier Indian Policy at the Crossroad*, 201–201.

18. "Led by Satanta." Wishart, David. (2007). *Encyclopedia of the Great Plains Indians,* 199–200. 180–181.

Battle of Little Bighorn

19. "Battle of Little Bighorn." Ibid., 117–118.

20. "Led by Sitting Bull." Ibid., 188–189.

21. "*Then why wonder at Indian difficulties.*" A quote by Phil Sheridan in *Annual Reports of the War Department* for year 1878, vol. 1.

22. "*Savage and civilized life cannot prosper.*" Report of the U.S. Commissioner of Indian Affairs,1881.

The Dawes or Allotment Act of 1887

23. "*I never knew a white man.*" A quote by Henry Dawes in Boughter, Judith A. (1968). *Betraying the Omaha Nation: 1790–1916,*134.

24. "Allotment or Dawes Act." Wishart, David. (2007). *Encyclopedia of the Great Plains Indians,* 199–200.18–19.

25. "*The irony and tragedy of the Omaha story.*" Boughter, Judith A. (1968). *Betraying the Omaha Nation: 1790–1916*, 8.

Malnutrition, Sickness, and Depression on the Reservation

26. "*When Susan La Flesche was a young girl on the reservation, she went to help care for a sick elderly Omaha woman.*" Starita, Joe. (2016) *A Warrior of the People*. 46.

Chapter Three—Dr. Susan La Flesche Picotte

Enter Dr. Susan La Flesche

1. "*On March 14, 1889.*" Starita, Joe. (2016). *A Warrior of the People,* back cover.

2. "Young Joseph lived in two worlds." Benson Tong (1999). *Susan La Flesche Picotte, MD: Omaha Indian Leader and Reformer,* 9–13.

3. "Susan's mother was Mary Gale." Ibid., 9–13.

4. "*My dear young daughters.*" A quote by Joseph La Flesche in Starita, Joe. (2016). *A Warrior of the People,* 58.

The Family of Joseph La Flesche

For more information on the La Flesche family, the book I would recommend is by Norma Kidd Green (1969) entitled: *Iron Eye's Family: The Children of Joseph La Flesche.*

5. "It was common Practice." Enss, Chris. (2006). *The Doctor Wore Petticoats: Women Physicians of the Old West.*

6. "She worked to establish libraries on the reservation." Starita, Joe. (2016). *A Warrior of the People,* 238.

7. "Susan's older sister Susette." Green, Norma Kidd. (1969). *Iron Eye's Family: The Children of Joseph La Flesche.* University of Nebraska Press.

8. "She was also called bright eyes," Wilson, Dorothy Clarke. (1974). *Bright Eyes: The Story of Susette La Flesche, an Omaha Indian.* McGraw Hill.

The Trial of Standing Bear

To learn more about Standing Bear and the trial of Standing Bear, the book "*I Am a Man*": *Chief Standing Bear's Journey for Justice* by Joe Starita is both comprehensive and well-written. Andrew Troy chose this book as his first reference in the movie he is currently producing on Standing Bear.

9. "Standing Bear." Wishart, David. (2007). *Encyclopedia of the Great Plains Indians,* 196–198.

10. *"The hand is not the color of yours."* Starita, Joe. (2008). A quote by Standing Bear in *"I Am a Man": Chief Standing Bear's Journey for Justice,* 151.

11. *"Indians are living souls."* A quote by Judge Elmer Dundy. Ibid., 155.

12. "Film-maker Andrew Troy." L Kent Wolgamott. (2022, December 18). Film Gets Jump-Start. *Lincoln Journal Star*

13. *"Far from disappearing."* Wishart, David. (2007). *Encyclopedia of the Great Plains Indians, 172.*

Wounded Knee Massacre

14. "Wounded Knee Massacre." Wishart, David. (2007). *Encyclopedia of the Great Plains Indians,* 222–224.

Susan La Flesche—The Early Years

The books by Joe Starita "*A Warrior of the People*" and Benson Tong "*Susan La Flesche Picotte, MD: Omaha Indian Leader and Reformer*" were both comprehensive, well-referenced reviews of Susan La Flesche's life and would be excellent choices for further reading.

15. *"To serve others, to visit the poor."* A quote by Susan La Flesche in Enss, Chris. (2006). *The Doctor Wore Petticoats: Women Physicians of the Old West.* 21.

Education at the Mission and Boarding School

Preparing to be a Physician-Medical Education in the 1880s

16. "In 1869, the position of a married woman was similar to that of a slave". A quote by Harriet Beacher Stowe in Starita, Joe. (2016). *A Warrior of the People,* 5.

17. "They were expected." Ibid., 19.

18. "*Resolved that no woman of true delicacy."* Enss, Chris. (2006). *The Doctor Wore Petticoats: Women Physicians of the Old West,* xii.

19. "As with many students, Susan liked the dissection lab." Starita, Joe. (2016). *A Warrior of the People,* 132.

Entering Medical Practice on the Omaha Reservation

20. "*One time an eight-year-old boy . . .*" Ibid., 162.

21. "Occupied 210 wood-frame houses . . ." Ibid., 166.

22. "*Easy to control.*" Ibid., 167.

Combining Her Medical Career with Marriage and Children

23. *"Henry was kind, considerate, and faithful."* Ibid., 193.

24. *"She was tall, slender, black eyed, and bore herself with an air of dignified authority that made her seem far less gentle than she proved to be. she was the most powerful public speaker he had ever heard."* A quote by John Neihardt in Starita, Joe. (2016) *A Warrior of the People,* p. 213.

25. Entertained legislatures." Ibid., 225–226.

Providing Medical Care for the Omaha Indians in the 1890s

Managing Trachoma

26. "Managing Trachoma." Mohammed P.M. , Abrishami, M., et al. (2016) Trachoma: Past, present, and future. J Curr Ophthalmol. 28(4), 165-169.

Assisting with Childbirth

27. "Assisting with Childbirth." Dary, David (2008). *Frontier Medicine: 1492–1941,* 174.

Opening the Walthill Hospital in 1913

28. "Walthill hospital." Benson Tong (1999). *Susan La Flesche Picotte, MD: Omaha Indian Leader and Reformer, 188–190.*

Chapter Four—Diagnostic Tools and Medicines in the 1890s

Diagnostic Tools in the 1890s

1. "Skin color and breathing pattern." Agnew, Jeremy. (2010). *Medicines in the Old West—A History, 1859–1900*, 5.

2. "Thermometers were broken." Ferris, Jeri. (1991). *Native American Doctor—The Story of Susan La Flesche Picotte,* 52.

3. "X-rays," Agnew, Jeremy. (2010). *Medicines in the Old West—A History, 1859–1900*, 129.

Diagnostic Tools Today

4. "Diagnostic tools today." Buttaro, T.M., Trybulski J., Polgar-Bailey, P. & Sandberg-Cook, J. (2017). *Primary Care: A Collaborative Practice.*

5. Ibid.

Vaccinations in the 1890s and Today

6. "Edward Jenner." Wells, Ken. (2007). *The History of Drugs: Vaccines.* Thomson Gale, 29–33.

7. "A Vaccine for Cholera." Ibid., 193–200.

Medications in the 1890s

8. "*Most medicines were primitive by today's standards.*" Agnew, Jeremy. (2010). *Medicines in the Old West—A History, 1859–1900*, 98.

9. "Medications in the 1890s." Agnew, Jeremy. (2010). *Medicines in the Old West: A History, 1859–1900;* Bollet, Alfred J. (2002). *Civil War Medicine: Challenges and Triumphs.* Galen Press; Bynum, W. & Bynum, H. (2011) *Great Discoveries in Medicine;* Dary, David. (2008). *Frontier Medicine: 1492–1941;* Loudon. (1997). *Western Medicine: An Illustrated History;* Porter, Roy. (2000) *Cambridge Illustrated History of Medicine;* Haller Jr., J.S. (1989). Opium usage in nineteenth century therapeutics. *Bulletin of* the *New York Academy of medicine, 65*(5), 591–607.

Medications that were available in the 1890s were listed in readings. However, there were few anecdotes in the readings describing Susan's use of specific medications. It was documented that Susan used both "modern" medicines and herbal medicines in her practice. Thus, in writing chapter four, I often identified medications that Susan could have used in treating her patients.

Medication Quackery

10. "Unscrupulous manufacturers." Dary, David (2008). *Frontier Medicine: 1492–1941,* 28–50.

11. *"Plenty of fresh air and sunshine."* A quote by Susan La Flesche in Mathes, Valerie Sherer. (1982). *Susan La Flesche Picotte: Nebraska's Indian Physician, 1865–1915,* 502.

Opium Addiction

12. *"Americans have become the greatest drug fiends in the world."* Miroff, Nick. (2017, October 17). From Teddy Roosevelt to Trump: How drug companies triggered an opioid crisis a century ago. *Washington Post.*

Medications Today

13. "Medications Today." Bartis, E., Briscoe, L., Fuseck, C., Lukez, S., Moeller, K. & Rich, E. (2014). *Drug Information Handbook for Advanced Practice Nursing.*

14. "The quality of lives today". Buttaro, T.M., Trybulski J., Polgar-Bailey, P. & Sandberg-Cook, J. (2017). *Primary Care: A Collaborative Practice.*

Chapter Five—The Germ Theory

Two books that I referred to often when writing chapters five through eight were: Kang, L. & Pedersen, N. (2021). *Patient Zero: A Curious History of the World's Worst Diseases* and Osterholm, M. & Olshaker, M. (2017). *Deadliest Enemy: Our War Against Killer Germs.*

The Tragic Consequences of the Columbian Exchange

1. *"Infectious disease is the deadliest enemy faced by all of mankind."* Osterholm, M. & Olshaker, M. (2017). *Deadliest Enemy: Our War Against Killer Germs,* 4.

2. *Countless lives have been lost.*" Loudon, Irvine (1997). *Western Medicine: An Illustrated History,* 177.

3. *"The entire history of the Americas might have played out differently if the disease transmission pattern had gone the other way."* Kang, L. & Pedersen, N. (2021). *Patient Zero: A Curious History of the World's Worst Diseases,* 153.

Infectious Diseases and the Omaha Tribe

Epidemiological Transition: Decrease in Death Rate from Infectious Diseases

4. *However, before 1930, infectious diseases got to people earlier and more often."* Osterholm, M. & Olshaker, M. (2017). *Deadliest Enemy: Our War Against Killer Germs,* 217.

Prior to knowledge of the Germ Theory, lack of sanitation had deadly results.

Lack of Sanitation During the Civil War

5. *"Because soldiers rarely had the opportunity to bathe."* Bollet, A.J. (2004). The major infectious epidemic diseases of Civil War soldiers. *Infectious Disease Clinics of North America*, 295.

Lack of Sanitation and the Omaha Indians

Prior to the 1800s, no one knew how best to prevent and treat infectious diseases.

Belief in Imbalance in the Four Humors

6. "Imbalance in humors." Agnew, Jeremy. (2010). *Medicines in the Old West—A History, 1859–1900*, 6-7.

Bloodletting, Blistering, and Purging

7. "Bloodletting, purging, and blistering." Ibid., 7.

8. "Bloodletting to treat an excess of blood." Ibid., 7.

9. *"The sicker the patient, the more blood was drained."* Ibid., 8.

10. "Mental illness not well understood" Ibid., *13–14.*

11. *"Purging the gut."* Ibid., 9.

12. *"Thunderclappers."* Ibid., 9.

13. *"Blistering."* Ibid., 10–11.

14. *"The remedy is worse than the disease."* A quote by Francis Bacon in Dary, David (2008). *Frontier Medicine: 1492–1941*, 28.

The Theory that "Miasma" Caused Infectious Diseases

15. "Diseases are not caused by Gods or demons." Altman, Linda Jacobs. (1998). *Plague and Pestilence: A History of Infectious Disease,* 14

16. "Bad air or miasma." Ibid.

17. "Concept of miasma pervasive." Kang, L. & Pedersen, N. (2021). *Patient Zero: A Curious History of the World's Worst Diseases,* 40.

18. "Real gains in sanitation. Ibid.

19. "Florence Nightingale," Ibid.

Knowledge of the Germ Theory revolutionized medical practice.

20. *"Leeuwenhoek."* Ibid., 44.

21. *"Lister."* Ibid., 247.

22. "Widely accepted in Europe." Richmond, Phyllis Allen. (1954). American attitudes toward the germ theory of disease 1860–1880. *Journal of the History of Medicine and Allied Sciences, 9*(4), 428–454.

23. "Koch discovered tuberculin vaccine." Kang, L. & Pedersen, N. (2021). *Patient Zero: A Curious History of the World's Worst Diseases,* 324.

24. "John Snow." Ibid., 288-292.

Causation and Spread of Infectious Disease

Causes of Infection: Bacteria and Viruses

25. "Bacteria and Viruses." Ibid., 44–49.

26. "Zoonotic diseases." Osterholm, M. & Olshaker, M. (2017). *Deadliest Enemy: Our War Against Killer* Germs, 65–68.

27. "Sanitation procedures." Ibid., 239–240.

28. "Multiple Problems in Sanitation." Starita, Joe. (2016) *A Warrior of the People,* 157,187, 233.

29. *"I will help the Omaha's physically, teach them the importance of cleanliness, order, and ventilation."* Enss, Chris (2006*). The Doctor Wore Petticoats: Women Physicians of the Old West,* 25.

30. *"Sanitation = Prevention."* Ibid., 233.

31. "Later in her life, promoted legislation." Tong, Benson. (1999). *Susan La Flesche Picotte, MD: Omaha Indian Leader and Reformer,* 181–182.

32. *"The spread of TB among my people is something terrible."* A quote by Susan La Flesche in Tong, Benson. (1999). *Susan La Flesche Picotte, MD: Omaha Indian Leader and Reformer,* 183.

33. "Opening of Walthill hospital." Ibid., 188–190.

Chapter Six—Tuberculosis

TB (TB): The Greatest Killer in History

1. "The deadliest disease throughout history." Kang, L. & Pedersen, N. (2021). *Patient Zero: A Curious History of the World's Worst Diseases,* 317.

2. "Present as long as humans have walked the earth." Ibid.

3. "Presentation, Causation, and Spread." Buttaro, T.M., Trybulski J., Polgar-Bailey, P. & Sandberg-Cook, J. (2017). *Primary Care: A Collaborative Practice,* 1264–1267.

4. *"Patient's waste away".* Osterholm, M. & Olshaker, M. (2017). *Deadliest Enemy: Our War Against Killer Germs,* 99.

5. *"TB patients were so weak that they were consumed."* Kang, L. & Pedersen, N. (2021). *Patient Zero: A Curious History of the World's Worst Diseases,* 319.

6. *"Mycobacterium TB."* Buttaro, T.M., Trybulski J., Polgar-Bailey, P. & Sandberg-Cook, J. (2017). *Primary Care: A Collaborative Practice,* 1262.

7. "Poor sanitation, overcrowding." Osterholm, M. & Olshaker, M. (2017). *Deadliest Enemy: Our War Against Killer Germs,* 99.

8. "TB not as contagious." Ibid., 108.

9. "Doc Holliday." Tanner, Karen Holliday. (1998). *Doc Holliday: A Family Portrait;* and Tennant, Forest. (2012). Doc Holliday: A story of TB, pain, and self-medication in the wild west. *Practical Pain Management.*

10. "20 percent of world's population." Kang, L. & Pedersen, N. (2021). *Patient Zero: A Curious History of the World's Worst Diseases,* 321.

11. "Emily Bronte." Ibid., 211.

12. "Robert Koch." Ibid., 324.

13. "One-quarter of Omaha people." Wishart, David. (1994). *An Unspeakable Sadness: The dispossession of the Nebraska Indians,* 153, 229.

14. "Communal drinking cup." Starita, Joe (2016). *A Warrior of the People,* 233.

15. "Thomas Ikinicapi." Ibid., 187.

16. "*She saw a young girl lying on the floor.*" Ibid., 21.

17. "Susan's brother-in-law and husband." Ibid., 221.

Vaccine and Treatment Today

18. "BCG vaccine." Kang, L. & Pedersen, N. (2021). *Patient Zero: A Curious History of the World's Worst Diseases,* 325.

19. "Antibiotics for TB." Buttaro, T.M., Trybulski J., Polgar-Bailey, P. & Sandberg-Cook, J. (2017). *Primary Care: A Collaborative Practice,* 1267–1270.

20. "Inactive TB." Ibid., 1264–1265.

21. "TB still a problem today." Osterholm, M. & Olshaker, M. (2017). *Deadliest Enemy: Our War Against Killer Germs,* 109.

22. "Danger of more TB in the future." Ibid., 110.

Chapter Seven—Influenza, Smallpox, and Measles

Influenza (the flu): More Deadly Than the Common Cold

1. "Presentation, Cause, Spread." Buttaro, T.M., Trybulski J., Polgar-Bailey, P. & Sandberg-Cook, J. (2017). *Primary Care: A Collaborative Practice,*1241–1242.

2. "Influenza Viruses." Kang, L. & Pedersen, N. (2021). *Patient Zero: A Curious History of the World's Worst Diseases,* 227.

3. "*The most dangerous places.*" Osterholm, M. & Olshaker, M. (2017). *Deadliest Enemy: Our War Against Killer Germs. 257.*

4. "Deadliest Flu Epidemics." Aronson, Virginia. (2000) *The Influenza Pandemic of 1918,* 106.

1918 Spanish Flu

5. "1918 Spanish Flu." Ibid., 111.

6. "Two billion people were stricken." Ibid., 103.

7. "Wearing masks." Kang, L. & Pedersen, N. (2021). *Patient Zero: A Curious History of the World's Worst Diseases,* 226.

8. "Dead bodies stacked." Aronson, Virginia. (2000) *The Influenza Pandemic of 1918,* 60–65.

9. "Strain of virus." Ibid., 39.

10. *"One patient."* Osterholm, M. & Olshaker, M. (2017). *Deadliest Enemy: Our War Against Killer Germs.* 258.

11. "Deaths due to pneumonia." Buttaro, T.M., Trybulski J., Polgar-Bailey, P. & Sandberg-Cook, J. (2017). *Primary Care: A Collaborative Practice,*1242–1243.

12. *"Bustling major cities."* Memories of the 1918 pandemic from those who survived. (2020, April 4). *New York Times.*

13. "Woodrow Wilson." Aronson, Virginia. (2000) *The Influenza Pandemic of 1918,* 91.

14. "Camp Funston." Kang, L. & Pedersen, N. (2021). *Patient Zero: A Curious History of the World's Worst Diseases,* 230.

15. "U.S. Public Health Dept." Aronson, Virginia. (2000) *The Influenza Pandemic of 1918,* 102.

16. "Flu epidemics on the Macy Reservation." Starita, Joe (2016). *A Warrior of the People,* 21.

Vaccine and Treatment Today

17. "Vaccines." Kang, L. & Pedersen, N. (2021). *Patient Zero: A Curious History of the World's Worst Diseases,* 227.

18. "Antiviral drugs." Buttaro, T.M., Trybulski J., Polgar-Bailey, P. & Sandberg-Cook, J. (2017). *Primary Care: A Collaborative Practice,*1242.

19. "It isn't 'if.'" Aronson, Virginia. (2000) *The Influenza Pandemic of 1918,* 25.

Smallpox (The Speckled Monster): The Disease Most Feared by Native Americans

Presentation, Causation Spread

20. "Presentation, causation, spread." Havemeyer, Janie. (2019). *Smallpox: How a Pox Changed History,* 11.
21. "Scarred for life." Ridgway, Tom. (2001). *Smallpox: Epidemics—Deadly Diseases Throughout History,* 11.
22. "Women in the 1700s." Agnew, Jeremy. (2010). *Medicines in the Old West—A History, 1859–1900,* 71–72.
23. "Pox diseases." Havemeyer, Janie. (2019). *Smallpox: How a Pox Changed History,* 8.
24. "One year outside of dead body." Havemeyer, Janie. (2019). *Smallpox: How a Pox Changed History,*16.

The Incident at Fort Pitt

25. "Incident at Fort Pitt." Ranlet, Philip. (2000). The British, the Indians, and Smallpox: What Actually Happened at Fort Pitt in 1763. *Pennsylvania History: A Journal of Mid-Atlantic Studies, 67*(3), 427–441
26. "Field Marshal Jeffrey Amherst." Osterholm, M. & Olshaker, M. (2017). *Deadliest Enemy: Our War Against Killer Germs,* 128.

The History of Smallpox

27. "Hernando de Soto." Ridgway, Tom. (2001). *Smallpox: Epidemics—Deadly Diseases Throughout History,* 23.
28. *"In the 1500s."* Osterholm, M. & Olshaker, M. (2017). *Deadliest Enemy: Our War Against Killer Germs,* 66.
29. "In 1639." Havemeyer, Janie. (2019). *Smallpox: How a Pox Changed History,*15.

Smallpox and the Omaha Tribe

30. "Lewis & Clark." Starita, Joe (2016). *A Warrior of the People,* 9.
31. "Continued to stalk." Ibid.

Vaccine Today

32. "Variolation." Havemeyer, Janie. (2019). *Smallpox: How a Pox Changed History,* 16.

33. "Washington defeated British." Ridgway, Tom. (2001). *Smallpox: Epidemics—Deadly Diseases Throughout History,* 30–32.

34. "Jenner discovered smallpox vaccine." Ibid., 35.

35. "As late as the 1960s and 1970s." Ibid., 5.

36. "Last case of smallpox." Kang, L. & Pedersen, N. (2021). *Patient Zero: A Curious History of the World's Worst Diseases,* 329.

37. "Dr. Henry Bedson." Ibid., 336.

38. *"To this day."* Ibid., 338.

Measles (Rubeola): Not Just a Disease of Children

Presentation, Causation, Spread

39. **"**Presentation, causation, spread." Kang, L. & Pedersen, N. (2021). *Patient Zero: A Curious History of the World's Worst Diseases,* 170.

40. **"**Complications of measles.**"** Lewis, Mark. (2020). Measles: *How a Contagious Rash Changed History,* 12.

41. "Leading cause of blindness." Ibid., 12.

42. "Measles (rubeola)." Kang, L. & Pedersen, N. (2021). *Patient Zero: A Curious History of the World's Worst Diseases,* 169.

43. "90 percent infection rate." Ibid.

History of Measles

44. *"Mortality rates from the newly introduced diseases were estimated to be between 60 and 95 percent."* Ibid., 147.

Measles and the Omaha Tribe

45. "Every two years." Lewis, Mark. (2020). Measles: *How a Contagious Rash Changed History,* 14.

46. "1888, measles on Macy reservation." Starita, Joe (2016). *A Warrior of the People,* 145.

47. "Vitamin A." Lewis, Mark. (2020). Measles: *How a Contagious Rash Changed History,* 13.

Vaccine and Treatment Today

48. "Vaccine." Kang, L. & Pedersen, N. (2021). *Patient Zero: A Curious History of the World's Worst Diseases,* 176.

49. "Clark County, Washington." Lewis, Mark. (2020). Measles: *How a Contagious Rash Changed History,* 28.

Chapter Eight—Typhoid Fever, Cholera, Dysentery

Typhoid Fever: The Four Fs: Feces, Food, Fingers, Flies.

1. *"The Four F's."* Jarrow, Gail (2015). *Fatal Fever; Tracking Down Mary Fallon*, 15.

Presentation, Causation, and Spread.

2. "Presentation, Causation, and Spread. Ibid., 15–16.

3. "Typhoid is Greek word for "foggy." Ibid., 19.

4. "Mortality rate 10 to 30 percent." Ibid., 15–16.

5. "Salmonella." Lynch, M., Blanton, E., Bulens, S., Polyak, C., Vojdani, J., Stevenson, J., et al. (2009). *"Typhoid fever in the United States, 1999–2006," JAMA, 392*(8), 859–865.

Typhoid Mary" Mallon (1869–1938)

6. "Asymptomatic Carrier." Jarrow, Gail. (2015*). Fatal Fever: Tracking Down Mary Fallon, 47.*

7. "George Soper." Altman, Linda Jacobs. (1998). *Plague and Pestilence: A History of Infectious Disease,* 81.

8. "*It's ridiculous to say I'm dangerous.*" Jarrow, Gail. (2015*). Fatal Fever: Tracking Down Mary Fallon,* 99.

9. "*The world was not very kind to Mary.*" Ibid., 129.

History of Typhoid Fever

10. "Typhoid came to America." Altman, Linda Jacobs. (1998). *Plague and Pestilence: A History of Infectious Disease,* 41.

11. "Lack of proper sanitation." Bollet, A.J. (2004). The major infectious epidemic diseases of Civil War soldiers. *Infectious Disease Clinics of North America,18,* 293–309.

12. "Purging the bowel." Agnew, Jeremy. (2010). *Medicines in the Old West—A History, 1859–1900,* 77.

13. "Famous people." Jarrow, Gail. (2015*). Fatal Fever: Tracking Down Mary Fallon,* 146–149.

14. "Filthy city." Harkins, Michael J. (1975). Public health nuisances in Omaha, *1870–1900. Nebraska History, 56.* 471–489.

15. "Typhoid In Lincoln, Nebraska." Waite, Herbert. H. (1913). Two Lincoln (Nebraska) typhoid fever epidemics of 1911 and 1912. *Faculty publications in the Biological Sciences,* 15–28.

Vaccine and Treatment Today

16. "Clean water." Jarrow, Gail. (2015*). Fatal Fever: Tracking Down Mary Fallon,* 138–143.

17. "Vaccine." Department of Health and Human Services. (10/30/19). *Vaccine Information Statement: Typhoid Vaccine.* Centers for Disease Control and Prevention.

18. "Treatment." Lynch et al., (2009) Typhoid Fever in the United States, 1999–2006, 864.

The Devastation of Cholera in the Frontier West

Presentation, Causation, and Spread

19. "Presentation, causation, spread." Kang, L. & Pedersen, N. (2021). *Patient Zero: A Curious History of the World's Worst Diseases,* 284.

20. "Roof gutter." Hayhurst, Chris. (2001). *Cholera: Epidemics-Deadly Diseases Throughout History,* 8.

21. "Die of their disease" Ibid., 9–10.

The Father of Epidemiology and Public Health—Dr. John Snow

22. *"Dr John Snow."* Kang, L. & Pedersen, N. (2021). *Patient Zero: A Curious History of the World's Worst Diseases,* 287–293; Osterholm, M. & Olshaker, M. (2017). *Deadliest Enemy: Our War Against Killer Germs,* 27–28; and Wright, Jennifer. (2017). *Get Well Soon: History's Worst Plagues and the Heroes Who Fought Them,* 131–143.

The History of Cholera

23. "1849 in Chicago." Hayhurst, Chris. (2001). *Cholera: Epidemics—Deadly Diseases Throughout History,* 9–10.

24. "James K. Polk." Kang, L. & Pedersen, N. (2021). *Patient Zero: A Curious History of the World's Worst Diseases,* 283.

Cholera along the Oregon Trail

25. "The Oregon Trail." Buck, Rinker. (2015). *The Oregon Trail: A New American Journey.*

26. "John C. Fremont." Chaffin, Tom. (2002). *Pathfinder: John Charles Fremont and the Course of American Empire.*

27. "Cholera along the trail." (April 2, 2019). *Doctors and Diseases on the Oregon trail—End of the Oregon trail. https://historicoregoncity.org/2019/04/02/doctors_and_diseases_on_the_oregon_trail.*

Cholera and the Plains Tribes

28. "Cholera and the Plains Tribes." Powers, Ramon & Leiker, James (Autumn 1998). Cholera among the Plains Indians: Perceptions, Causes, and Consequences. *Western Historical Quarterly*. 29(3) 317.

29. "*How many thousands of NA's died in this disaster cannot be known.*" Annual Reports of the Commissioner of Indian Affairs: 1826–1932.

30. "1,234 Pawnee died." Cholera and the Plains Tribes." Powers, Ramon & Leiker, James (Autumn 1998). Cholera among the Plains Indians: Perceptions, Causes, and Consequences. *Western Historical Quarterly*. 29(3) 322.

31. "People who had died." Ibid.

32. "Wolves partially devoured." Ibid., 323.

33. "One-fourth of the Osage tribe." Ibid., 325.

34. "*We were sorry later that we permitted the white travelers to go through the plains.*" *A* Quote by a Native American from the Kiowa tribe in Powers, Ramon & Leiker, James (Autumn 1998). Cholera among the Plains Indians: Perceptions, Causes, and Consequences. *Western Historical Quarterly*. 29(3) 337.

Vaccine and Treatment Today

35. "Clean Water Act of 1972." Hayhurst, Chris. (2001). *Cholera: Epidemics-Deadly Diseases Throughout History*, 29.

36. "Doxycycline and others." Bartis, E., Briscoe, L., Fuseck, C., Lukez, S., Moeller, K. & Rich, E. (2014). *Drug Information Handbook for Advanced Practice Nursing* (15th ed.).

37. "Well-developed water systems". Hayhurst, Chris (2001). *Cholera: Epidemics-Deadly diseases Throughout History.*

Dysentery: Loose Stools and More

Presentation, Causation, and Spread

38. "Symptoms of dysentery." Pfeiffer, Margaret L., Dupont, Herbert L. & Ochoa, Theresa J. (April,2012). The patient presenting with acute dysentery—a systemic review. *Journal of Infection*. 64(4), 375.

39. *"I felt slightly ill for two to four weeks."* Agnew, Jeremy (2010). *Medicine in the Old West: A History,* 65.

40. *" Shigella."* Dupont, Herbert L. (2015). *Bacillary Dysentery* in *Mandell, Douglas, and Bennett's Principles and Practices of Infectious Diseases.* 8th ed., 2569.

41. "When diarrhea is severe." Pfeiffer, Margaret L., Dupont, Herbert L. & Ochoa, Theresa J. (April,2012). The patient presenting with dysentery—a systemic review. *Journal of Infection.* 64(4), 375.

History—Dysentery During the Civil War

42. "Dysentery during the Civil War." Bollet, A.J. (2004). The major infectious epidemic diseases of Civil War soldiers. *Infectious Disease Clinics of North America, 18,* 293–309.

43. "Soldiers called dysentery." Ibid., 296.

44. "Fatality for chronic dysentery." Ibid., 297.

45. "Meals lacking in nourishment" Trimble, Marshall (June 3, 2020). Disease in the Frontier Army. *True West Magazine,* 3. *https://truewestmagazine.com/disease-in-the-frontier-army/*

46. "Opium, quinine, and brandy." Ibid.

47. "Cholera along the trail." (April 2, 2019). *Doctors and Diseases on the Oregon trail—End of the Oregon trail. https://historicoregoncity.org/2019/04/02/doctors_and_diseases_on_the_oregon_trail.*

Dysentery and the Omaha Tribe

48. "Sweet flag," Starita, Joe. (2016). *A Warrior of the People,*17.

Vaccine and Treatment Today

49. "Fluoroquinolone." Dupont, Herbert L. (2015). *Bacillary Dysentery* in *Mandell, Douglas, and Bennett's Principles and Practices of Infectious Diseases.* 8th ed., 2569.

50. "Research is ongoing." Ibid.

51. "Recommendations from the Center for Disease Control." Hayhurst, Chris. (2001). *Cholera: Epidemics-Deadly Diseases Throughout History,* 39–40.

Chapter Nine—Historical Trauma

Historical Trauma or "Trauma of the Soul"

1. *"26 percent of Nebraska Indians perceive their health as only fair or as poor."* (2020) Office of Health Disparities and Health Equity. (2020). *BRFSS 2011-2015,* 103.

2. "Compared to all other races, Native Americans in Nebraska Indians have the highest death rates from alcohol." Ibid., p. 205.

3. *"Populations subjected to long-term mass trauma exhibit a higher prevalence of disease even generations after the original trauma."* Sotero, M.M. (2006). A conceptual model of historical trauma: implications for public health practice and research. *Journal of Health Disparities Research and Practice.* 93.

4. *"The past is never dead. It's not even past."* A quote by William Faulkner in Lawless, Jill. *(January 8, 2023).* "Royal Revelations." *Lincoln Journal Star,* A5.

5. "Theory first developed by." Brave Heart, Maria Yellow Horse (1998-06-01). The return to the sacred path: Healing the historical trauma and historical unresolved grief response among the Lakota through a psychoeducational group intervention. *Smith College Studies of Social Work.*

6. "In the 1500s." Crosby, Alfred. (1972). *The Columbian Exchange: Biological and Cultural Consequences of 1492.*

Federal Boarding Schools—Forgiving the Unforgivable

7. "On March 3, 1819, the U.S. Congress passed an Act to provide education for the purpose of providing against further decline and extinction." Lajimodiere, Denise (2019*). Stringing Rosaries: The History, the unforgivable, and the Healing of Northern Plains American Indian Boarding School Survivors,* 9–10.

8. "Separated during the formative years of their lives." Ibid., 10.

9. *"The removal of children from their families is considered one of the most devastating traumas that occurred to the Indian people."* Braveheart," M.Y.H. & DeBruyn, L.M. (1998). The American Indian Holocaust: Healing historical unresolved grief. *American Indian and Alaska Native Mental Health Research.*

10. "There were eight boarding schools in Nebraska." Lajimodiere, Denise (2019*). Stringing Rosaries: The History, the unforgivable, and the Healing of Northern Plains,* Appendix A.

11. "Rigid military rules." Ibid., 11.

12. *"Withhold rations, clothing, and other annuities from Indian parents or guardians who refused or neglected to send and keep their children in school."* Ibid., 10–11.

13. "The cutting of hair. Ibid.,121.

14. "Overwhelming feeling of loss." Ibid., 13.

15. "A Native American boarding school survivor from North Dakota." Ibid., 119–130.

16. "*The stories were unbelievable.*" Ibid., 276.

Addiction to Alcohol in Indians as a Response to Generations of Historical Trauma

One book that I used to review causes and treatments for alcohol addiction was Harrison and Connery's *The Complete Family Guide to Addiction.* The book is useful and easy to read for both lay people and professionals.

17. "*While addicts may be able to avoid.*" Harrison, T. & Connery, H. (2019). *The Complete Family Guide to Addiction*, 13.

18. "Greater genetic susceptibility." Enoch, M.A. & Goldman, D (2001). The genetics of alcoholism and alcohol abuse. *Current Psychiatry Reports.*

19. "Stressful situation." Goh, C. & Agius, M. (2010), The stress-vulnerability model: How does stress impact on mental illness at the level of the brain and what are the consequences? *Psychiatria Danubia.*

Treatment for Alcohol Addiction Today

20. "Effective programs today often combine therapy and counseling with medications." Huebner, R. & Kantor, L. (2011) Advances in alcoholism treatment. *Alcohol Research Health.*

Susan's La Flesche's Fight against Alcohol Abuse

21. "She requested that liquor sales be prohibited." Starita, Joe. (2016) *A Warrior of the People,* p. 229.

Susan's Fight to Prevent Historical Trauma

22. "Even today, compared to other races, Nebraska Indians are more likely to be diagnosed with depression. Office of Health Disparities and Health Equity. (2020). *BRFSS 2011–2015,* 218.

23. *"These Omaha need help in many aspects of life."* Enss, Chris (2006*). The Doctor Wore Petticoats: Women Physicians of the Old West, 27.*

24. "A *virtual chief without having a title. Her word was higher law in the tribe than that of the Indian agent."* Ferris, Jeri (1991*). Native American Doctor: The Story of Susan La Flesche Picotte,* 73.

Current Treatments for Health and Behavioral Problems Related to Historic Trauma

25. "Acknowledging a long history of official degradations." 111th Congress (2009-2010). *Senate Joint Resolution 14.* U.S. Government Printing Office.

Susan La Flesche: The Last Days of a Remarkable Leader

26. "Buried in Bancroft Cemetery. "Tong, Benson (1999). *Susan La Flesche Picotte, MD: Omaha Leader and Reformer,* 190.

27. *"We are confronted here."* A quote by Harry Keefe in Starita, Joe. (2016) *A Warrior of the People,* 274.

28. "Education, service, stewardship, and justice." Tong, Benson (1999). *Susan La Flesche Picotte, MD: Omaha Indian and Reformer,* 199.

29. *"Her public accomplishments are a reminder that color and culture are no barriers to success and respect."* A quote by U.S. House Representative Doug Bereuter in Tong, Benson (1999). *Susan La Flesche Picotte, MD: Omaha Indian and Reformer,* 198.

30. "I feel blessed by the privilege." A quote by Susan La Flesche in Tong, Benson (1999). *Susan La Flesche Picotte, MD: Omaha Indian and Reformer,* 198.

Chapter Ten—The Omaha People Today

1. "Sons Caryl and Pierre." This information was obtained during a discussion with descendants of Joseph La Flesche, including Carolyn Johnson, the great-granddaughter of Marguerite La Flesche Diddock and Susan Picotte, the great-granddaughter of Susan La Flesche Picotte. I so appreciate the time they spent with me.

2. "Walthill hospital." (Retrieved March 25, 2023). *www.drsusancenter.org.*

The People of the Omaha Tribe are Surviving!

3. "In the 2020 federal census, 5,247 Americans were enrolled as Omaha Indians." Bureau of the Census. (2020) *United States Census—April 1,2020 to October 16, 2020.*

4. "In 2020, median household income for Nebraska Indians was $25,700." Office of Health Disparities and Health Equity. (2020). *BRFSS 2011-2015,* 55.

The Omaha People continue to practice traditions of their tribe.

5. "The Omaha People continue to practice traditions of their tribe." This information was obtained in the fall of 2022 from Nancy Gillis, a Native American who lives in the town of Walthill and is a well-known speaker and advocate for Native Americans. I want to express a very sincere thank-you to Nancy Gillis. She is providing a valuable service to the Omaha tribal people.

The Health Statistics for Nebraska Native Americans, including the Omaha tribe.

6. *"As with other Nebraskans, most Nebraska Indians die of cancer and heart disease."* Office of Health Disparities and Health Equity. (2020). *BRFSS 2011-2015,* 41.

7. *"Compared to other Nebraskans, Nebraska Indians are more likely to die from unintentional injuries (such as motor vehicle accidents, alcohol-related deaths, and poisonings), liver disease, and diabetes mellitus."* Ibid.,110.

8. "Nebraska Indians continue to have more physical and mental health problems." Ibid., 220–221.

9. *"Flu and pneumonia vaccination rates are higher for Nebraska Indians than for other Nebraskans."* Ibid., 228.

Federally recognized tribes on reservations do have the right to govern themselves, their lands, and their people.

The Native American Rights Fund.

More Assistance with Health Care Needs is now Available.

The Proud History of the Omaha People.

10. "The proud history of the Omaha Indians." La Flesche, F. & Fletcher, A. (1972). *The Omaha Tribe.*

Attitudes of Americans and policies of the U.S. Government are changing.

11. *We cannot correctly understand the present,"* A quote by Dennis Hastings in Tong, Benson (1999). *Susan La Flesche Picotte, MD: Omaha Leader and Reformer,* xii.

12. "*Honoring and empowering.*" Ibid.

Honoring Native Americans—The First Inhabitants of Nebraska and our Nation

Preserving Native American Language, Culture, and Traditions

13. "*The old ways are not devoid of values, culture, and emotional ties. They need to always be preserved.*" A quote by Susan La Flesche in Enss, Chris. (2006). *The Doctor Wore Petticoats: Women Physicians of the Old West, 21.*

14. *"The ACLU recently affirmed their support."* Reist, Margaret (2023, February 14). "Native Advocates Say They've Been Silenced." *Lincoln Journal Star.*

Publishing Tribal Customs and Traditions

15. *"They need to know their history, and they don't."* A quote by Margery Coffee in Hytrek, Nick. (2023, January 29). "Efforts Underway to Publish Tribe's History." *Lincoln Journal Star.*

The Adopt-A-Buffalo Program

16. "The Adopt-A-Buffalo program" Brown, Matthew. (2022, November 23). "Tribes Expanding Buffalo Herds." *Lincoln Journal Star.*

17. *"When the buffalo went away, the hearts of my people fell to the ground, and they could not lift them up again."* A quote by Crow Chief Plenty Coups in Smits, David (Autumn,1994). *The Frontier Army and the Destruction of the Buffalo: 1865–1883*

A Kindergarten through High School Cultural Learning Program

18. *"In 2020, only 69 percent of Nebraska Indians had obtained a high school degree, and 3.2 percent who were enrolled in high school withdrew before completion."* Office of Health Disparities and Health Equity. (2020). *BRFSS 2011-2015,* 74.

19. *"The story at the Santee school is a story of how the Santee Sioux students can persevere."* A quote by Redwing Thomas in Trudell, Tim (2022, December 4). "Learning their Culture helps Santee Students." *Lincoln Journal Star.*

Incorporating Native Americans into U.S. society as Knowledgeable, Empowered, and Belonging Equals

Providing More Educational Opportunities

Including Native Americans in Decision Making

Americans are electing more indigenous people to local, state, and federal offices.

20. "In-person summit." (2022, December 1). "Tribal Summit." *Lincoln Journal Star.*

We Are Still Here. We Shall Remain.

Bibliography

Alcohol and Addictions

Book

Harrison. T. & Connery, H. (2019). *The Complete Family Guide to Addiction*. The Guillford Press.

Journals

Dozier, E.P. (1966). "Problem drinking among American Indians: The role of sociocultural deprivation." *Quarterly Journal of Studies on Alcohol, 27*(1), 77–87.

Dube, Shanta. et al. (2002). "Adverse childhood experiences and Personal alcohol abuse as an adult." *Addictive Behaviors, 27*(5), 713–725.

Enoch, M.A. & Goldman, D. (2001). "The genetics of alcoholism and alcohol abuse." *Current Psychiatry Reports, 3*(2), 144–151.

Goh, C. & Agius, M. (2010). "The stress-vulnerability model: How does stress impact on mental illness at the level of the brain and what are the consequences?" *Psychiatria Danubia, 22(*2), 198–202.

Goodwin, D.W. (1985). "Alcoholism, and genetics: The sins of the fathers." *Archives of General Psychiatry, 42,* 171–174.

Huebner, R. & Kantor, L. (2011). "Advances in alcoholism treatment." *Alcohol Research Health, 33*(4), 295–299.

Prescott, C.A. & Kendler, K.S. (1999). "Genetic and environmental contributions to alcohol abuse and dependence in a population-based sample of male twins." *American Journal of Psychiatry, 156*(1). 34–40.

Suddendorf, Ronald. (1989), "Research on alcohol metabolism among Asians and its implications for understanding causes of alcoholism." *Public Health Reports, 104*(6), 615–620.

Battle of Little Bighorn

Book

Kershaw, Robert (2005). *Red Sabbath: The Battle of Little Bighorn*. Ian Allan Publishing.

Bleeding, Purging, and Blistering

Book

Steele, Volney. (2005). *Bleed, Blister, and Purge: A History of Medicine on the American Frontier*. Mountain Press Publishing.

Boarding Schools

Books

Adams, David Wallace. (1995). *Education for Extinction: American Indians and the Boarding School Experience, 1875–1928.* University Press of Kansas.

La Flesche, Francis. (1978). *The Middle Five: Indian Schoolboys of the Omaha Tribe.* University of Nebraska Press-Bison Books.

Lajimodiere, Denise K. (2019). *Stringing Rosaries: The History, the Unforgivable, and the Healing of Northern Plains American Indian Boarding School Survivors.* North Dakota State University Press.

Journal
Dodd, Johnny. (2022, August 29). "I was abused at a Native American school." *People*, 62–63.

Newspapers
Lawless, Jill- Associated Press. (January 8, 2023). "Royal Revelations." *Lincoln Journal Star*, A5.

"Native Americans Recall Trauma." (2022, October 16). *Lincoln Journal Star.*

Reist, Margaret. (2023, February 14). "Native Advocates Say They've Been Silenced." *Lincoln Journal Star.*

Wade, Jessica. (2022, November 21). "Making It Right." *Omaha World Herald.*

Documents
Indian Affairs: Laws and Treaties, vol. 2. (1904) Kappler, Charles, ed. U.S. Government Printing office.

Cholera

Books
Hayhurst, Chris. (2001). *Cholera: Epidemics-Deadly Diseases Throughout History.* Rosen Publishing Co., Inc.

Kang, L. & Pedersen, N. (2021). *Patient Zero: A Curious History of the World's Worst Diseases.* Workman Publishing.

Wright, Jennifer. (2017). *Get Well Soon: History's Worst Plagues and the Heroes who fought them.* Henry Holt & Co

Current Diagnostic Tests and Medications

Books

Bartis, E., Briscoe, L., Fuseck, C., Lukez, S., Moeller, K. & Rich, E. (2014). *Drug Information Handbook for Advanced Practice Nursing* (15th ed.). Lexicomp.

Buttaro, T.M., Trybulski J., Polgar-Bailey, P. & Sandberg-Cook, J. (2017). *Primary Care: A Collaborative Practice.* (5th ed). Elsevier, Inc.

Ferri, F. (2018). *Ferri's Clinical Advisor.* Elsevier.

Dawes "Allotment" Act

Books

Otis, Delos Socket. (1973). *The Dawes Act and the Allotment of Indian Lands,* (F.P. Prucha, ed). University of Oklahoma Press.

Washburn, Wilcomb E. (1975). *The Assault on Indian Tribalism: The General Allotment Law (Dawes Act) of 1887*, (H.H. Hyman, ed.). Lippincott.

Journal

Stremlau, Rose. (2005). "To domesticate and civilize wild Indians: Allotment and the campaign to reform Indian families, *1875–1887.*" *Journal of Family History, 30,* 265–286.

Dysentery

Books

Bollet, Alfred J. (2002). *Civil War Medicine: Challenges and Triumphs.* Galen Press.

Dupont, Herbert L. (2015). *Bacillary Dysentery* in *Mandell, Douglas, and Bennett's Principles and Practices of Infectious Diseases.* 8th ed. Elsevier.

Journals

Bollet, A.J. (2004). “The major infectious epidemic diseases of Civil War soldiers.” *Infectious Disease Clinics of North America,18,* 293–309.

Pfeiffer, Margaret L., Dupont, Herbert L. & Ochoa, Theresa J. (April,2012). “The patient presenting with acute dysentery—a systemic review.” *Journal of Infection. 64*(4),

Trimble, Marshall (June 3, 2020). “Disease in the Frontier Army.” *True West Magazine. https://truewestmagazine.com/disease-in-the-frontier-army/*

Economic and Cultural Dispossession of Native Americans

Books

Boughter, Judith A. (1998). *Betraying the Omaha Nation: 1790–1916.* University of Oklahoma Press.

Wishart, David. (1994). *An Unspeakable Sadness: The dispossession of the Nebraska Indians.* University of Nebraska Press.

Government Document

Report of the U.S Commissioner of Indian Affairs. (1881) U.S. Government Printing Office.

Family of Joseph La Flesche

Books

Crary, Margaret. (1973). *Susette La Flesche: Voice of the Omaha Indians.* Hawthorne Books.

Green, Norma Kidd. (1969). *Iron Eye's Family: The Children of Joseph La Flesche.* University of Nebraska Press.

Wilson, Dorothy Clarke. (1974). *Bright Eyes: The Story of Susette La Flesche, an Omaha Indian.* McGraw Hill.

Frontier Medicine

Books

Agnew, Jeremy. (2010). *Medicines in the Old West: A History, 1859–1900.* McFarland & Company, Inc.

Dary, David. (2008). *Frontier Medicine: 1492–1941.* Random House.

Loudon, I. (1997). *Western Medicine: An Illustrated History.* Oxford University Press.

Porter, Roy. (2000) *Cambridge Illustrated History of Medicine.* Cambridge University Press.

George Catlin

Books

Gurney, George & Heyman, Therese, eds. (2002). *George Catlin and His Indian Gallery*. Washington, D.C., Smithsonian American Art Museum

Hassrick, Royal. (1997). *The George Catlin Book of American Indians.* Promontory Press.

McCracken, Harold. (1959). *George Catlin and the Old Frontier*. Dial Press.

Germ Theory

Book

Osterholm, M. & Olshaker, M. (2017) *Deadliest Enemy: Our War Against Killer Germs*. Little, Brown Spark.

Journal

Richmond, Phyllis Allen. (1954). "American attitudes toward the germ theory of disease 1860–1880." *Journal of the History of Medicine and Allied Sciences, 9*(4), 428–454.

Herbal Therapies—Native American Philosophy of Health

Books

Cichoke, Anthony J. (2001). Secrets *of Native American Herbal Remedies.* Avery—A Member of Penguin Putnam, Inc.

Farrar, Jon. (2011). *Field Guide to Wildflowers of Nebraska and the Great Plains.* (2nd ed). University of Iowa Press.

Gilmore, Melvin R. (1977). *Uses of Plants by the Indians of the Upper Missouri River Region.* University of Nebraska Press.

Heatherley, Ana N. (1998). *Healing Plants: A Medicinal Guide to Native North American Plants and Herbs.* Lyons Press.

Simmons, M. & Irving, J. (2016). *The Gardener's Companion to Medicinal Plants.* Francis Lincoln Limited.

Trafzer, C. & Weiner, D. (2001). *Medicine Ways: Disease, Health, and Survival Among Native Americans.* Altamira Press: Rowman & Littlefield Publishers, Inc.,

Historical Trauma

Journals

Brave Heart, Maria Yellow Horse (1998-06-01). "The return to the sacred path: Healing the historical trauma and historical unresolved grief response among the Lakota through a psychoeducational group intervention." *Smith College Studies in Social Work, 68*(3), 287–305.

Brave Heart, M.Y.H. & DeBruyn, L.M. (1998). "The American Indian holocaust: Healing historical unresolved grief." *American Indian and Alaska Native Mental Health Research, 8*(2), 60–82.

Sotero, M.M. (2006). "A conceptual model of historical trauma: implications for public health practice and research." *Journal of Health Disparities Research and Practice, 1*(1), 93–108.

Whitbeck, L., Adams, G., Hoyt, D. & Chen, X. (2004). "Conceptualizing and measuring historical trauma among American people." *American Journal of Community Psychology, 33* (3/4), 119–130.

Government Documents

111th Congress (2009–2010). *Senate Joint Resolution 14.* U.S. Government Printing Office.

History of Infectious Disease

Books

Altman, Linda Jacobs. (1998). *Plague and Pestilence: A History of Infectious Disease.* Enslow Publishers, Inc.

Bynum, W. & Bynum, H. (2011) *Great Discoveries in Medicine.* Thames & Hudson.

Crosby, Alfred. (1972). *The Columbian Exchange: Biological and Cultural Consequences of 1492.* Greenwood.

Duffy, John. (1953). *Epidemics in Colonial America.* Louisiana State University Press.

Kang, L. & Pedersen, N. (2021). *Patient Zero: A Curious History of the World's Worst Diseases.* Workman Publishing.

Kunitz, Stephen J. (1993). "*Disease and Mortality in the Americas since 1700*" in *The Cambridge World History of Human Disease.* (ed. Kenneth F. Kiple). Cambridge University Press. 328–334.

Osterholm, M. & Olshaker, M. (2017). *Deadliest Enemy: Our War Against Killer Germs*. Little, Brown Spark.

Ostler, Jeffrey. (2019). *Surviving Genocide: Native Nations and the United States from the American Revolution to Bleeding Kansas*. Yale University Press.

Journal

Crosby, Alfred W. (1976). "Virgin soil epidemics as a factor in the Aboriginal depopulation in America." *William and Mary Quarterly, 33*(2). 289–299.

Honoring and Empowering Native Americans

Newspapers

Brown, Matthew. (2022, November 23). "Tribes Expanding Buffalo Herds." *Lincoln Journal Star.*

Hytrek, Nick. (2023, January 29). "Efforts Underway to Publish Tribe's History." *Lincoln Journal Star.*

"Tribal Summit." (2022, December 1). *Lincoln Journal Star.*

Trudell, Tim (2022, December 4). "Learning Their Culture Helps Santee Students." *Lincoln Journal Star.*

Influenza

Books

Aronson, Virginia. (2000) *The Influenza Pandemic of 1918*. Chelsea House Publishers.

Buttaro, T.M., Trybulski J., Polgar-Bailey, P. & Sandberg-Cook, J. (2017). *Primary Care: A Collaborative Practice.* (5th ed). Elsevier, Inc.

Kang, L. & Pedersen, N. (2021). *Patient Zero: A Curious History of the World's Worst Diseases.* Workman Publishing.

Osterholm, M. & Olshaker, M. (2017). *Deadliest Enemy: Our War Against Killer Germs.* Little, Brown Spark.

Starita, Joe. (2016) *A Warrior of the People.* St. Martin's Griffin.

Wright, Jennifer. (2017). *Get Well Soon: History's Worst Plagues and the Heroes who fought them.* Henry Holt & Co

Journal

Adams, Mikaela. (2020) "A Very Serious and Perplexing Epidemic of Grippe: The Influenza of 1918 at the Haskell Institute." *American Indian Quarterly, 44(1).*

Newspaper

"Memories of the 1918 pandemic from those who survived." (2020, April 4). *New York Times.*

John Charles Fremont

Books

Chaffin, Tom. (2002). *Pathfinder: John Charles Fremont and the Course of American Empire.* Hill & Wang.

Spence, Mary. (1973). *The Expeditions of John Charles Fremont.* vol. 2. University of Illinois Press.

Lewis & Clark Expedition

Books

Ambrose, Stephen E. (1996). *Undaunted Courage: Meriwether Lewis, Thomas Jefferson, and the Opening of the American West.* Touchstone.

McIntosh, Elaine N. (2003). *The Lewis & Clark Expedition*. Sioux Falls Center for Western Studies.

Moulton, Gary E. (ed.) (2001). *The Journals of the Lewis and Clark Expedition*. (vols. 1 to 13). University of Nebraska Press.

Ronda, James P. (1984). *Lewis and Clark Among the Indians.* University of Nebraska Press.

Louisiana Purchase

Book

Sprague, Marshall. (1974). *So Vast, So Beautiful a Land: Louisiana and the Purchase.* Little, Brown.

Measles

Books

Kang, L. & Pedersen, N. (2021). *Patient Zero: A Curious History of the World's Worst Diseases.* Workman Publishing.

Lewis, Mark. (2020). Measles: *How a Contagious Rash Changed History.* Capstone Press.

Starita, Joe. (2016) *A Warrior of the People.* St. Martin's Griffin.

Journals

Davis, R.M., Whitman, E.D., Orenstein, W.A., Preblud, S.R., Markowitz, L.E. & Hinman A.R. (1987). "A persistent outbreak of measles despite appropriate prevention and control measures." *American Journal of Epidemiology, 126*(3), 438–49.

Greenwood, Major. (1988). "Epidemics and Crowd-Diseases: Measles. By Major Greenwood, 1935." *Review of Infectious Diseases, 10*(2), 492–499.

Medications in Use in the 1890s

Books

Agnew, Jeremy. (2010). *Medicines in the Old West: A History, 1859–1900.* McFarland & Company, Inc.

Bollet, Alfred J. (2002). *Civil War Medicine: Challenges and Triumphs.* Galen Press.

Bynum, W. & Bynum, H. (2011) *Great Discoveries in Medicine.* Thames & Hudson.

Dary, David. (2008). *Frontier Medicine: 1492–1941.* Random House.

Loudon, I. (1997). *Western Medicine: An Illustrated History.* Oxford University Press.

Porter, Roy. (2000) *Cambridge Illustrated History of Medicine.* Cambridge University Press.

Robson, Barry & Baek, 0.K. (2009). *The Engines of Hippocrates: From the Dawn of Medicine to Medical and Pharmaceutical Informatics.* John Wiley & Sons.

Journals

Haller Jr., J.S. (1989). "Opium usage in nineteenth century therapeutics." *Bulletin of* the *New York Academy of medicine, 65*(5), 591–607.

Gay, G.R., Inaba, D.S., Sheppard, C.W. & Newmeyer, J.A. (1975). "Cocaine: History, epidemiology, human pharmacology, and treatment, a perspective on a new debut for an old girl." *Clinical toxicology. 8*(2), 149–178.

Newspapers
"The Colorful History of Pills Can Fill Many a Tablet." (September 19, 2015). *Los Angeles Times.*

Miasma

Books
Kang, L. & Pedersen, N. (2021). *Patient Zero: A Curious History of the World's Worst Diseases.* Workman Publishing.

Osterholm, M. & Olshaker, M. (2017). *Deadliest Enemy: Our War Against Killer Germs.* Little, Brown Spark.

Journals
Aavind, M. & Chung, K. (2010). "Evidence-based medicine and hospital reform: Tracing origins back to Florence Nightingale." *Plastic Reconstructive Surgery, 125(*1), 403–409.

Halliday, Stephen. (2001). "Death and miasma in Victorian London: An Obstinate belief." *BMJ, 323,* 1469–1471.

Native American Lifestyle

Books
Moulton, Candy. (2001). *Everyday Life Among the American Indians: 1800–1900.* Writer's Digest Books.

Mullins, G. (2019). *Native American Cooking: An Indian Cookbook with Legends and Folklore.* (2nd ed). Light of the Moon Publishing.

Wishart, David. (2007) *Encyclopedia of the Great Plains Indians.* University of Nebraska Press.

Journal

Smits, David. (Autumn 1994). "The Frontier Army and the Destruction of the Buffalo: 1865–1883." *The Western Historical Quarterly*, 25(3): 312–338.

Omaha Tribe

Books

Anderson, Madelyn Klein. (2000). *The Omaha.* Franklin Watts, A Division of Grolier Publishing.

La Flesche, F. & Fletcher, A. (1972). *The Omaha Tribe.* (2 vols.). (Original work published in 1911). University of Nebraska Press.

Documents

Office of Health Disparities and Health Equity. Division of Public Health. (2020) *Nebraska BRFSS 2011–2015.* Nebraska Dept of Health and Human Services.

National Center for Health Statistics. (2020). *National Vital Statistics System.*

Bureau of the Census. *United States Census—April 1,2020 to October 16, 2020.* Department of Commerce.

Opium Abuse

Journals

Haller Jr., J.S. (1989). "Opium usage in nineteenth century therapeutics." *Bulletin of the New York Academy of medicine, 65*(5), 591–607.

Kandall, S.R. (2010). "Women and drug addiction: A historical perspective." *Journal of Addictive Diseases, 29(*2), 117–126.

Lyden, J. & Binswanter, I. (2019). "The United States Opioid Epidemic." *Semin Perinatal.* 43(3), 123–131.

Newspapers

Labianca, D.A. & Reeves, W.J. (1984). "Drug Dependency: A Legacy from the Past." *USA Today, 112*(2466), 90–92.

Little, B. (2021, December 7). "How Civil War Medicine Led to America's First Opioid Crisis." *Inside History Newsletter.*

Miroff, Nick. (2017, October 17). "From Teddy Roosevelt to Trump: How Drug Companies Triggered an Opioid Crisis a Century Ago." *Washington Post.*

Oregon Trail

Book

Buck, Rinker. (2015). *The Oregon Trail: A New American Journey*. Simon & Schuster.

Peyote and the Native Americans

Books

La Barre, Weston. (1971). *The Peyote Cult*. Schocken Books. (3rd Printing).

Stewart, Omer C. (1987). *Peyote Religion: A History*. University of Oklahoma Press.

Journal

Hill, Thomas W. (1990, Fall). "Peyotism and the control of heavy drinking: The Nebraska Winnebago in the early 1900s." *Human Organization, 49*, 255–265.

Government Document

American Religious Freedom Act. Public Law 103–344. (1994, October 5). U.S. Government Printing Office.

Phil Sheridan

Book

Hutton, Paul Andrew. (1985) *Phil Sheridan and His Army.* University of Nebraska Press.

Government Document

Annual Reports of the War Dept for year 1878, vol. 1. (1878). U.S. Government Printing office.

Plains Indians

Books

Lowery, Linda. (2017) *North American Indian Nations: Native Peoples of the Plains.* Lerner Publications.

Miller, Alfred Jacob. (1973). *Braves and Buffalo: Plains Indian Life in 1837.* University of Toronto Press.

Wishart, David. (2007) *Encyclopedia of the Great Plains Indians.* University of Nebraska Press.

Public Health

Books

Kang, L. & Pedersen, N. (2021). *Patient Zero: A Curious History of the World's Worst Diseases.* Workman Publishing.

Osterholm, M. & Olshaker, M. (2017) *Deadliest Enemy: Our War Against Killer Germs.* Little, Brown Spark.

Reservation System

Book

Trennert, Robert A. Jr. (1975). *Alternative to Extinction: Federal Indian Policy and the Beginnings of the Reservation System, 1846–51.* Temple University Press.

Sacred Pole

Book

Ridington, Robin & Hastings, Dennis. (1997). *Blessing for a Long Time: The Sacred Pole of the Omaha Tribe.* University of Nebraska Press.

Sanitation and Infectious Disease in the Civil War

Book

Bollet, Alfred J. (2002). *Civil War Medicine: Challenges and Triumphs.* Galen Press.

Journal

Bollet, A.J. (2004). "The major infectious epidemic diseases of Civil War soldiers." *Infectious Disease Clinics of North America,18,* 293–309.

Sitting Bull

Book

Utley, Robert M. (1993). *The Lance and the Shield: The Life and Times of Sitting Bull.* Henry Holt

Smallpox

Books

Havemeyer, Janie. (2019). *Smallpox: How a Pox Changed History.* Capstone Press.

Hopkins, D. (1983). *Princes and Peasants: Smallpox in History.* University of Chicago Press.

Kang, L. & Pedersen, N. (2021). *Patient Zero: A Curious History of the World's Worst Diseases.* Workman Publishing.

Osterholm, M. & Olshaker, M. (2017) *Deadliest Enemy: Our War Against Killer Germs.* Little, Brown Spark.

Ridgway, Tom. (2001). *Smallpox: Epidemics—Deadly Diseases Throughout History.* Rosen Publishing Co., Inc.

Wright, Jennifer. (2017). *Get Well Soon: History's Worst Plagues and the Heroes who fought them.* Henry Holt & Co

Journals

Dollar, Clyde D. (1977). "The high plains smallpox epidemic of 1837–1838." *Western Historical Quarterly,* 8(1), 15–38.

Ranlet, Philip. (2000). "The British, the Indians, and Smallpox: What Actually Happened at Fort Pitt in 1763." *Pennsylvania History: A Journal of Mid-Atlantic Studies, 67*(3), 427–441.

Newspaper

Rimmer, Monica. (2018, August 10). "How Smallpox Claimed Its Final Victim." *BBC News.*

Standing Bear

Book

Starita, Joe. (2008). *"I am a Man": Chief Standing Bear's Journey for Justice.* St. Martin's Press.

Newspaper

L Kent Wolgamott. (2022, December 18). "Film Gets Jump-Start." *Lincoln Journal Star.*

Susan La Flesch Picotte

Books

Ferris, Jeri. (1991). *Native American Doctor: The Story of Susan La Flesche Picotte.* Carolrhoda Books, Inc.

Starita, Joe. (2016) *A Warrior of the People.* St. Martin's Griffin.

Tong, Benson. (1999). *Susan La Flesche Picotte, MD: Omaha Indian Leader and Reformer.* University of Oklahoma Press.

Wilkerson, J.L. (1999). *Dr. Susan La Flesche Picotte: A Doctor to her People.* Acorn Book.

Journals

Mathes, Valerie Sherer. (1982). "Susan La Flesche Picotte: Nebraska's Indian Physician, 1865–1915." *Nebraska History, 63,* 502–530.

Mathes Valerie Sherer (1983, Summer) "Susan La Flesche Picotte M.D.: Nineteenth-Century Physician and Reformer." *Great Plains Quarterly, 113,* 172–196.

Mohammad PM, Abrishami M, et al. (2016). Trachoma: Past, present, and future. *J Curr Ophthalmol.* 28(4):165–69.

Newspaper

"Walthill Hospital Designated a National Landmark." (2022, April 5) *Norfolk Daily News.*

Transcontinental Railroad

Books

Ambrose, Stephen E. (2000) *Nothing like It in the World: The Men who Built the Transcontinental Railroad: 1863–1869.* Simon & Schuster.

White, Richard. (2012). *Railroaded: The Transcontinental and the Making of Modern America*. W.W. Norton.

Newspapers

Davis, Theodore R. (1867, December 14). "Buffalo Hunting: Shooting Buffalo from the Trains of the Kansas Pacific Railroad." *Harper's Weekly.*

Tuberculosis

Books

Buttaro, T.M., Trybulski J., Polgar-Bailey, P. & Sandberg-Cook, J. (2017). *Primary Care: A Collaborative Practice.* (5th ed). Elsevier, Inc.

Bynum, H. (2012). *Spitting blood—The History of TB.* Oxford University Press.

Kang, L. & Pedersen, N. (2021). *Patient Zero: A Curious History of the World's Worst Diseases.* Workman Publishing.

Lewis, Mark. (2020). *TB: How the White Death Changed History.* Capstone Press.

Osterholm, M. & Olshaker, M. (2017). *Deadliest Enemy: Our War Against Killer Germs.* Little, Brown Spark.

Tanner, Karen Holliday. (1998). *Doc Holliday: A Family Portrait.* University of Oklahoma Press.

Wright, Jennifer. (2017). *Get Well Soon: History's Worst Plagues and the Heroes who fought them.* Henry Holt & Co

Journals

Hoeppner, V.H. & Marciniuk, D.D. (2000). "TB in Aboriginal Canadians." *Can. Respir. J., 7*(2), 141–146.

Mackowiak, Philip et al. (2005). "On the origins of American TB." *Clinical infectious Diseases, 41*(4). *doi.org/10.1086/432013.*

Tennant, Forest. (2012). "Doc Holliday: A story of TB, pain, and self-medication in the wild west." *Practical Pain Management, 12*(11).

Typhoid Fever

Books

Agnew, Jeremy. (2010). *Medicines in the Old West—A History, 1859–1900,*

Altman, Linda Jacobs. (1998). *Plague and Pestilence: A History of Infectious Disease.* Enslow Publishers, Inc.

Harris, J.B., Ryan, E.T. (2020). *Typhoid fever, paratyphoid fever, and typhoidal fevers.* Bennett J.E., Dolin R., Blaser M.J., (eds.)

Mandell, Douglas, and Bennett's Principles and Practice of Infectious Diseases, (9th ed.) Elsevier, chapter 100.

Jarrow, Gail. (2015). *Fatal Fever: Tracking Down Mary Fallon.* Calkin Creek: An Imprint of Highlights.

Leavitt, Judith Walzer. (2014). *Typhoid Mary: Captive to the Public's Health.* Beacon Press,

Wright, Jennifer. (2017). *Get Well Soon: History's Worst Plagues and the Heroes who fought them.* Henry Holt & Co.

Journals

Bollet, A.J. (2004). "The major infectious epidemic diseases of Civil War soldiers." *Infectious Disease Clinics of North America, 18,* 293–309.

Harkins, Michael J. (1975). "Public health nuisances in Omaha, 1870–1900." *Nebraska History, 56*. 471–492.

Lynch, M., Blanton, E., Bulens, S., Polyak, C., Vojdani, J., Stevenson, J., et al. (2009). "Typhoid fever in the United States, 1999–2006." *JAMA, 392*(8), 859–865.

Soper, George A. (1939). "The Curious Career of Typhoid Mary." *Bulletin of the New York Academy of Medicine, 15*(10), 698–712.

Waite, Herbert. H. (1913). "Two Lincoln (Nebraska) typhoid fever epidemics of 1911 and 1912." *Faculty publications in the Biological Sciences,* 418.

Government Documents

Centers for Disease Control and Prevention. *Vaccine Information Statement: Typhoid Vaccine (*10/30/19). Department of Health and Human Services.

Report on the origin and spread of typhoid fever in U.S, military camps during the Spanish war of 1898. (1904). vol. 2. U.S. Government Printing office.

Vaccines

Books

Brundle, Joanna. (2021). *Vaccines: Lifesaving Medicine.* Enslow Publishing, Inc.

Osterholm, M. & Olshaker, M. (2017) *Deadliest Enemy: Our War Against Killer Germs.* Little, Brown Spark.

Warren Wagon train Raid

Journal

Hamilton, Allen (1986). "The Warren Wagon train Raid: Frontier Indian Policy at the Crossroad." *Arizona and the West, 28*(3), 201–224.

Women Physicians / Women in the Victorian Era

Books

Beecher, C. & Beecher, H. (1869). *The American Woman's Home.* J.B. Ford & Co.

Chambers, Peggy. (1938) *A Doctor Alone: A Biography of Elizabeth Blackwell, the First Woman Doctor, 1821–1910.* Abelard-Schuman.

Enss, Chris. (2006). *The Doctor Wore Petticoats: Women Physicians of the Old West.* Morris Book Publishing, LLC.

Roth Walsh, Mary. (1977). *Doctors Wanted: No Women need Apply: Sexual Barriers in the Medical Profession.* Yale University Press.

Wounded Knee

Books

Starita, Joe. (2016) *A Warrior of the People.* St. Martin's Griffin.

Utter, Jack. (1991). *Wounded Knee & the Ghost Dance Tragedy.* (1st ed.). National Woodlands Publishing Company.

Index

Nancy Waltman retired in 2021 and is a Professor Emeritus from the University of Nebraska College of Nursing. She has lived with her husband Lou in Lincoln, Nebraska, for over forty years. Nancy and Lou have two sons, Luke and Clint, and both sons work in the areas of information technology and computers. Although Nancy was the primary author, every member of the Waltman family helped with the research and the writing of this book. Luke and Clint served as computer and technology experts. Lou was the official driver for the trips to the Macy Reservation and to libraries, museums, and events in Omaha, Nebraska. He also took some of the photos for the book. Since this book was a family project, below is a picture of the family.

The Waltman Family
Family members in the photo include, from left to right, Luke, Nancy, Lou, and Clint Waltman. The photo was taken at Pioneers Park in Lincoln. Dedicated in 1930, the landscape architect for the park was Ernest Herminghaus. The park includes corridors to views of the Nebraska State Capital and a system of recreational paths. Pioneers Park was listed on the National Register of Historic Places in 1993. Photo by Shadlee Meinke Photography, LLC.